THE SCIENCE OF
GENETICS

THE SCIENCE OF
GENETICS

BY Charlotte Auerbach

DRAWINGS BY
Inge G. Auerbach Linker

HARPER TORCHBOOKS   *The Science Library*
Harper & Row, Publishers, New York, Evanston, and London

THE SCIENCE OF GENETICS

First HARPER TORCHBOOK edition published 1964 by
·Harper & Row, Publishers, Incorporated
New York, Evanston, and London.

Library of Congress Catalog Card Number: 61-6429.

Contents

Contents

Preface

THE PURPOSE and scope of this little book have been set out fully in its first chapter. They may be summarized here as follows.

It has not been my intention to provide an entertaining account of the most recent discoveries in genetics: the double helix of DNA, genetic coding, bacterial transformation, "killers" in Paramecium, sexual processes in bacteria and viruses, etc. These exciting discoveries find their modest place in the late chapters. Anybody who wants more information on them can get it from the many excellent popular articles, lectures, films, and television programs that are devoted to topical biology.

But it is my firm conviction that a clear grasp of the elements of genetics is indispensable to anybody who wants to take away from such educational occasions more than a few awe-inspiring technical terms, a few intriguing three-letter words like DNA and RNA, and a hazy conviction that modern geneticists are doing wonderful things. It is my intention to provide the indispensable knowledge without which the most recent advances in genetics cannot be understood.

I do not wish to imply, however, that this book forms only a prelude to what is really valuable and interesting in genetics. Quite to the contrary, I believe that all aspects of genetics are fascinating in their own right, that many of them take us right up to the fundamental problems of life, and that others are deeply interwoven with problems of human health and happiness. In addition, all of them are exciting. Sixty years ago Mendel's laws and thirty years ago Muller's success in producing mutations by X rays were as hot news as the structure of DNA is in our day.

I have tried to be as clear and simple as possible and have used no more technical terms than are necessary for accuracy and clarity. But genetics is not a descriptive science like natural history. It has to be *understood,* as physics and chemistry have to be understood. For this, co-operation on the reader's side is indispensable. Only readers who are willing to give this co-operation will profit from this book; I hope that these readers will be satisfied with it. The many illustrations are meant to help them grasp difficult points. Some of the illustrations may seem too playful for a scientific book; but with the exception of chapter headings and endings every drawing has been designed carefully as a help to the reader.

CHARLOTTE AUERBACH

Institute of Animal Genetics, Edinburgh
February, 1961

Acknowledgments

A NUMBER of colleagues have helped me generously with advice and criticism. My special thanks are due to Dr. G. H. Beale, F.R.S., and Dr. D. S. Falconer, both of this Institute, who between them read the whole of the manuscript and made many helpful suggestions and critical remarks. They are, of course, not responsible for any errors I may have committed nor for the personal opinions expressed in some of the chapters. I also wish to express my gratitude to Professor Alexander Brink of the University of Wisconsin and to Dr. G. F. Sprague of the United States Department of Agriculture, who very kindly supplied me with literature and data on hybrid corn. The quotation on Ancon sheep in Chapter 7 was taken from an article by Walter Landauer and Tso Kan Chang in *Jour. Hered., 40* (1949); the data on criminality in Chapter 17 from an article by Paul Popenoe in *Jour. Hered., 27* (1936); and the data on freckling and rickets in the same chapter from papers by von Verschuer.

I am very grateful to Dr. B. M. Slizynski of the Institute of Animal Genetics and to Miss Patricia Jacobs of the Western General Hospital in Edinburgh for the photographs of chromosomes in Plates II (except II, 8) and III, and to Dr. D. von Wettstein of the Genetics Department of the Forestry Institute in Stockholm for the electron micrograph of a chloroplast (Plate VI, 1) and for his help in the construction of a diagram of the steps involved in chloroplast formation (Fig. 72).

Grateful acknowledgment is also made for the use of the following illustrations: Plate II, 8 from M. Westergaard, *Arveligheds-laeren,* Copenhagen, Munksgaard, 1953. Plate III, 1 from A. Lima-de-Faria, *Chromosoma, 5,* 1 (1952). Plate III, 3 from P. Chesley, *Jour. Exptl. Zool., 70,* 429 (1935). Plate III, 4 from H. P. Donald et al., *Brit. Vet. Jour., 108,* 227 (1952). Plate III, 5 from C. Wriedt and O. L. Mohr, *Jour. Genetics, 20,* 187 (1928). Plate IV, top, from W. F. Lamoreux, *Jour. Hered., 32,* 221 (1941). Plate IV, bottom, from F. B. Hutt, *Genetics of the Fowl,* McGraw-Hill, 1949, courtesy of M. S. Pease. Plate V, 1 from F. J. Kallmann and G. Sander, *Jour. Hered., 39,* 349 (1948). Plate V, 2 from H. Grüneberg, *Genetics of the Mouse,* 2nd edition, The Hague, Martinus Nijhoff, 1952. Plate VI, 2 and Plates VII, 1 and 3 from S. E. Luria, *General Virology,* John Wiley & Sons, 1953. Plate VII, 4 from T. F. Anderson, *Cold Spring Harbor Symp. Quant. Biol., 18,* 197 (1953). Plate VII, 5 from C. F. Robinow, *Experimental Cell Research* (Stockholm), Suppl. 1, 204 (1949). Plate VIII, 1 from R. L. Cuany, A. H. Sparrow and V. Pond *Zeitschrift für induktive Abstammungs-und Vererbungslehre, 89,* 7. Plate VIII, 2 from C. R. Stockard and O. D. Anderson, *Amer. Anat. Memoir,* No. 19 (1941).

Fig. 37 from R. W. Winters et al., *Trans. Ass. Amer. Physicians, 70,* 234 (1957). Fig. 44 from G. Melchers and A. Lang, *Biologisches Zentralblatt, 67,* 105 (1948). Fig. 45 freely drawn from halftone plates in M. Gordon, *Endeavour, 9,* 26 (1950). Fig. 53 abbreviated from F. J. Kallmann and D. Reisner, *Jour. Hered., 34,* 293 (1943). Fig. 77 traced from V. M. Ingram and A. O. W. Stretton, *Nature* (Lond.), *184,* 1903 (1959). Fig. 78 traced from J. D. Watson and F. H. C. Crick, *Cold Spring Harbor Symp. Quant. Biol., 18,* 123 (1953). Fig. 79 from C. Auerbach, *Genetics in the Atomic Age,* Oxford Univ. Press, 1955. Fig. 84 traced from A. Romer, *Man and the Vertebrates,* Univ. of Chicago Press, 1941, p. 144.

C. A.

CHAPTER 1 *What Genetics Is About*

THE READER, on being presented with a book, wants to have an idea of what the book is likely to contain. The question: What is genetics about? is not easy to answer, very much less so than, for instance, the question as to what zoology or geology is about. Instead of trying to answer it I shall let the reader listen in on a conversation among the geneticist (G), a physician (P), a farmer (F), and a schoolboy (S). This should give him a pretty good idea of what he is going to find in this book, and it should help him decide whether or not he wants to read it.

P: I looked up my dictionary to find out how it defines genetics. It says: the science of heredity. Would you agree to this?

G: On the whole I would. The *study of heredity* certainly was the beginning of genetics and is still, so to speak, its centerpiece. But modern genetics includes much more than a study of heredity, at least of what is commonly called heredity.

S: Let's see what the dictionary has to say about heredity. Here it is: "the tendency of like to beget like." I expect this means simply that white sheep have white lambs and black sheep black ones.

F: But white sheep may have black lambs.

S: Well, that's not heredity then.

F: I don't know about that; you may get black lambs in some

1

herds of white sheep and not in others. So there seems something of heredity in it.

G: You are quite right: it is heredity pure and simple which makes black lambs come out in some matings between white sheep and not in others. Don't overlook that the definition in the dictionary (which is not a very good definition anyhow) speaks only of a "tendency" of like to beget like. Very often the offspring is unlike the parents, and very often this, too, is due to heredity.

P: As when dumb children are born from hearing parents.

G: Yes, this is frequently a case of heredity.

F: Aren't then the grandparents often deaf? Or uncles or aunts?

G: Yes, that's true. This makes it important to go into the family history if one wants to give advice to parents who are afraid of having a child with some hereditary disability.

P: Are there definite rules by which you can tell whether or not a child will have such a disability?

G: Well, not exactly. We can hardly ever foretell the fate of any given child with certainty. But we can often give the parents a good idea of the risk they run of having a disabled child.

F: I expect you can do the same for the agriculturist who has some hereditary disease cropping up in his herd, like dropsy in the Ayrshire cattle?

G: Yes, in such cases the geneticist may be of great help to the animal breeder. In fact his predictions can be much more precise than for children, because in animals he can carry out progeny tests.

S: Well, I must say all this sounds pretty negative to me. Just getting rid of bad heredity. Is this all genetics can do for us? What about something positive, like making us into better people?

G: Geneticists have quite a good idea of how they might go about doing it; but they will meet with great difficulties, not the least of which will be opposition from many members of the society. Meanwhile they have to be content with making better agricultural plants and animals.

F: But has not man done this from his very beginning, long before he knew anything about genetics?

G: True. And he has even used much the same methods which we still use: picking the best specimens for breeding, and discarding the worst.

F: Also crossing strains to combine the most useful features of both in their progeny.

G: Yes, all these are very old, prescientific methods. Only we can now get them to work much more quickly and efficiently because we have a better idea of what we are doing. Also we have worked out quite a few new tricks from our knowledge of genetics. Progeny testing, for example. Or hybrid maize.

F: I believe some plant-breeding institutes have made new useful varieties by X rays or chemicals.

P: Have they, now? And we are always shouted at for using X rays because this will produce idiots in future generations.

G: There is no real contradiction here. A very little knowledge of genetics will make this clear.

But let us stop here for a moment. I want you to realize that with the last point raised we have left the subject of heredity in its strict sense. I mean we no longer ask "How are hereditary traits transmitted?"—which is the basic question of the science of heredity. We ask "How does new hereditary variation arise?" This is a much more modern question, and one which plays an outstanding role in present-day genetical research.

S: That is called *mutation research,* is it not?

G: Quite right. You will hear a good bit about it in this book.

S: Will we hear whether drinking of coffee makes mutations?

G: Well, that is a remote possibility. It might be tested on mice. But there are more important questions in mutation research.

P: I have often heard that there is a connection between mutation research and the study of cancer.

G: There is. A very close one, in fact, especially with cancer therapy. Perhaps mutation research may also help us to understand how cancer arises.

P: I should like to raise a very different point. There has been quite a stir in medical journals about people suffering from certain types of intersexuality.

S: Meaning when a woman turns into a man?

P: No, not that. I mean people who are sexually not fully developed and to some extent resemble the opposite sex. It seems there is something wrong with the chromosomes of such people. Does this mean that these conditions are hereditary?

G: Not in the sense that they are inherited, but rather that the mechanism of inheritance has gone wrong.

F: Are they the same as freemartins in cattle? I mean the sterile female twins of male calves?

G: No, those have a different origin. But I am very glad these points have been brought up because they take us into a very important field of genetical research. This is the study of *sex determination*.

F: Do you mean the study of how the development of a male differs from that of a female?

G: No, that is a problem of embryology. What I mean are questions like these: Why is it that in most animal species there are about as many males as females born? Can we do anything to influence the sex of the offspring after it has been conceived?

F: You can, in bees.

G: Not really. You can only change a worker bee into a queen bee, but both are females. You cannot change a drone into a queen.

F: No, this you cannot do. But you can arrange to have fewer or more queens or drones by providing the right type of cells for the eggs.

G: Yes, in this sense you are right. In fact, the way in which sex is determined in bees is quite different from that in most animals.

P: What about the fact that many more men are color-blind than women? I read in an old textbook of ophthalmology that this is due to women having more practice in handling colored materials, but this does not seem likely. I expect it must have something to do with this genetical basis of sex you mentioned just now.

G: Indeed it has. Color blindness of the type you mean—that is, red-green color blindness—is quite simply a hereditary abnormality, whose inheritance is mixed up with the inheritance of sex.

P: I expect its being hereditary makes it incurable.

G: Oh, no, although this is a very common misconception. There is nothing in a hereditary disease which makes it inherently less curable than a nonhereditary one.

P: Could you give us an example of a curable hereditary disease?

G: I could give many. For instance, diabetes.

F: Is that the disease that makes the body unable to deal with sugar?

P: Yes, it is. And it is now usually curable by insulin. But I never knew it was hereditary.

G: You might not think so from looking at the family histories of diabetes. In fact what is inherited is not the disease itself, but a tendency to develop it. Whether or not this tendency will get its way depends on the way of life of such a person, mainly on his diet.

P: Well, if you call that a hereditary disease, then you might also call tuberculosis hereditary; for the tendency to contract it definitely runs in families. But obviously this cannot be right.

G: Why not?

P: Well, because we know that tuberculosis is caused by a bacillus and not by heredity.

G: Yes, but a lot of people get in contact with this bacillus and only some become ill. Whether or not they do depends on many things; for instance, the way they are housed and fed. It also depends to a large degree on an inherited susceptibility. There are many cases like this in which both an external cause and an inherited tendency to respond produce a disease.

F: What about intelligence? Do we inherit intelligence or only a tendency to become intelligent?

G: This depends on how you define intelligence. I should say we inherit an ability to profit mentally from education and experience, but how far this ability will be developed depends on the conditions of our life, especially on the education we get.

F: Probably in the same way as it depends on the way you look after your cows whether they will yield all the milk they are capable of yielding.

G: Precisely.

F: But this raises a difficult practical problem. How do I know whether a cow is a good milker because I am a good farmer or because she is a good cow?

S: Why do you want to know? As long as you get the milk—

F: I want to know because I want to decide whether I should breed from her.

G: Now you have brought up the old problem of heredity versus environment, or nature versus nurture. This is not only of the greatest importance for the animal and plant breeder; it also determines much of our attitude toward our children and fellow beings. For example, if we believe that there is a strong hereditary element in criminality—

S: Is there?

G: You will read about this later on. But whatever conclusion we come to, it must necessarily influence our attitude toward crime and criminals. The study of the relative roles of *heredity and environment* in making living beings into what they are is a very important topic of genetics.

S: I know. That is where the twin studies come in.

G: Quite right.

F: I am afraid I must ask a rather silly question. You speak so glibly about inheriting "tendencies." That sounds rather mystical to me. I should like to think of my inheritance as something more tangible than tendencies. But of what am I to think?

S: I know: genes.

F: Hm, I have heard that term before, but I am afraid it does not mean much more to me than a sound. Can you tell me what these genes are?

G: I am afraid I can't, at least not precisely. As a matter of fact, we have learned quite a lot about them recently, but you can read this in a later chapter. For the moment it will be sufficient to say that they are large molecules. Each germ cell carries thousands of them, and each one carries its own specification for some developmental process, say for the formation of the bones or of the brain. So we start life with a kind of miniature code of instructions on how to develop.

P: And how well these instructions are being followed depends on our environment?

G: Yes, that is quite a neat way of formulating the nature-nurture relationship.

P: But who is there to decipher the code and carry out instructions?

G: The living substance of the cell, what we call the cytoplasm. How the cytoplasm does the deciphering of the code and how it translates it into the creation of more living substance, of biological form and activity, is one of the two great mysteries of life. It is being studied intensively by biochemists and geneticists all over the world, but we are still very far from a solution. At least this is so for the initial steps: the decoding and the first chemical reactions in the cell. On the other hand, we know quite a lot about the way genes affect later steps in development. Hereditary abnormalities, such as taillessness in mice, have been traced far back into embryonic life, and the chemical background for genetical differences in many plant colors has been very successfully analyzed. These investigations form the field of *physiological genetics;* in higher organisms, this includes *embryological genetics* as a special area.

P: I should imagine that if we go far enough back in such analysis we will always end up with biochemical effects of genes.

G: Precisely. What we call *biochemical genetics* has become the most important branch of physiological genetics. In the past ten years or so these investigations have derived tremendous impetus from the opening up of microorganisms for the study of genetics.

F: Do you mean bacteria?

G: Bacteria and molds or other fungi. Also some algae. Such simple organisms lend themselves more readily to biochemical analysis than most higher organisms. One may, for example, find that one strain of fungus can make a vitamin that other strains cannot make because they lack one or more of the necessary genes. Then, by comparing the chemistry of these various strains one can often learn something about the chemical processes by which this substance is made in the organism. In fact, biochemistry has profited at least as much from *microbial genetics* as microbial genetics from biochemistry.

F: I find it difficult to imagine genetical work with microorganisms. I thought it always required crossing.

G: Ah, but microorganisms can be crossed.

P: Perhaps fungi can; I am afraid I know very little about their life history. But I remember very clearly from my student days that bacteria have no sexual processes.

G: You will be surprised to find out that they have not only one, but several, all of them very unorthodox. You did not learn this as a student because all this has been discovered very recently. It may surprise you even more to hear that viruses, too, have their own version of sex.

P: You do indeed stagger me. I used to think of viruses as some halfway house between living and nonliving.

S: May I ask something which I have been dying to ask for the past ten minutes?

G: Certainly.

S: You said that the way the gene transmits its information to the cell is one of the two great mysteries of life. What is the other one?

G: The way each gene makes another gene just like itself. This happens whenever a cell divides, and as a result exact copies of all the genes which the embryo has received from its parents will be found in every cell of the adult organism. This, of course, includes the germ cells, and through them copies of the same genes are transmitted to the next generation, and so it goes on indefinitely. This second great mystery of life is bound up with the unique *nature of the gene,* and many scientists—geneticists, chemists, even physicists—are at present trying to find out what this is.

But I am afraid our time is almost up. I only want to mention one further aspect of genetics, and certainly not its least important one. This is the role it plays in our understanding of evolution. Darwin constructed the framework for his theory of evolution without knowledge of even the elements of genetics. It was an imposing structure, but it had quite a few weak spots. By applying our knowledge of genetics to the interpretation of *evolution* we have made Darwin's framework into as solid a structure as is humanly possible for a theory that deals with facts of the past.

P: If I may tie the end of our discussion to its beginning, I should like to say this: you certainly have made it clear that modern genetics is much more than a study of heredity. It seems to span the whole width and breadth of the living world, from the nature of the gene to evolution.

S: And it seems to come nearer to the mystery of life than any other science.

F: As a practical man I want to add that it seems to have applications to many more fields of human life than I had imagined: not only to agriculture, but also to education, to the prevention of disease, to our attitude toward criminality, and so on.

G: I am very glad that this discussion has made you aware of all these aspects of genetics. We have touched on them in rather a haphazard way, and I think it may be useful to you if I end up by giving you a very brief outline of the order in which the different topics will be arranged in this book.

S: I must say this is a jolly good idea. I got rather mixed up between twins and viruses and evolution.

G: Well, then, we shall start with the laws of heredity. We shall do this by following the genes from generation to generation without inquiring much into their nature beyond the fact that they are the material carriers of hereditary transmission. As a part of this study of heredity we shall deal with sex determination. And, of course, we shall have quite a lot to say about practical applications of genetics, both positive and negative ones. Next we shall try to bridge the gap between the gene and the trait—or character, as we usually say—that it determines. We shall start to build this bridge at the far end, the one we can observe. First of all, we shall have to consider the influence of environment on the expression of hereditary characters, and here twin research will play its role. Next we shall look at the way genes influence development. The nearer this takes us to the gene the more shall we become involved in biochemical genetics. Here we shall find it very useful to consider examples from the genetics of microorganisms. Finally, we shall reach a region which is still largely unknown territory, the region where the gene exercises its mysterious functions of making other genes in its own image and of transmitting its information to the cytoplasm. To throw some light into this region we shall use information from many sources: from chemistry, physics, and of course also genetics, especially mutation research and virus genetics. Not all this will be of purely theoretical interest. Microbial genetics has many applications to human affairs, such as the production of high-yielding strains of Penicillium or the study of the poliomyelitis virus that causes infantile paralysis. It is hardly necessary to point out the practical value of mutation research in the atomic age.

CHAPTER 2 *Gregor Mendel*

DURING THE YEARS 1854–1868 the students in the secondary school of Brünn (Brno in modern Czechoslovakia) had an Augustine monk as teacher of physics and natural history. The name of this monk was Gregor Mendel (Plate I). In his spare time Mendel grew peas in the garden of his monastery. He did not grow them for the refectory meals, but in order to study the laws of inheritance. He was, of course, not the first scientist to attempt this; but all previous attempts had failed to clarify the subject. The reason why Mendel succeeded where others had consistently failed is that he possessed to the highest degree two of the essential abilities which go into the making of a scientist: the ability to ask the right question from Nature, and the ability to interpret Nature's answer correctly. In addition, he was exceedingly patient and painstaking, two qualities which by themselves do not make a good scientist, but without which even an outstanding mind rarely achieves a good scientific record. Mendel worked for eight years and raised and examined in great detail about 10,000 pea plants before he published his results in a modest communication to a local scientific society. This happened on February 8, 1865, and although it took the scientific world thirty-five years to realize its importance, we now consider this day the birthday of modern genetics.

Mendel's predecessors crossed—or "hybridized"—varieties of plants which differed from each other in many ways. The results were bewildering and defied interpretation. Mendel realized that the only way to get a clear answer from Nature is to put to her a very simple question. He therefore chose for hybridization strains of peas which differed from each other in only one clear-cut feature or "character," for example, the shape of the seeds or the color of the flowers. This allowed him not only to classify the progeny quite unambiguously in respect to the chosen difference; he could also *count* how many individuals belonged in the one class, how many in the other. This quantitative method of investigation was the key to his success; but it also made his results incomprehensible and suspect to his contemporaries, as it has made them incomprehensible and suspect in our times to Lysenko in Russia.

Let us study Mendel's procedure from one of his experiments. A cross was made between plants with wrinkled and plants with round seeds (peas) by fertilizing flowers of one strain with pollen taken from the other and having the fertilized flowers develop into pods with peas. The seed of a plant arises from the union of a female germ cell, the ovule, with a male germ cell, the pollen grain, in the same way as the embryo of an animal arises from the union of an ovum (egg) with a spermatozoon (semen cell). The seed, therefore, is the child of the plant, and the seeds which set on the hybridized pea plants were their children, or the "first-generation hybrids." All seeds without exception were round, independent of whether the plant on which they grew came from the round-pea strain fertilized with pollen from the wrinkled-pea strain or vice versa. Thus, of the two contrasting characters of the parent strains, only one appeared in the hybrid. The other one, however, was not lost; as we shall see presently, it reappeared in the next generation. Mendel called the character which came through in the hybrid "dominant" and the one which was temporarily lost "recessive" (from the verb recede). By this definition, round is the dominant, wrinkled the recessive character. Next Mendel took 253 round hybrid seeds, grew them into plants and left these plants to flower and set seed by natural self-fertilization. The new seeds were the grandchildren of the original plants used for the cross; they are called the "second-generation hybrids." Mendel counted and classified all of them. There were 7,324 seeds, of which 5,474 were round and 1,850 were wrinkled. Most pods contained both kinds of seed, but since there were altogether so many more round than wrinkled ones, Mendel was not surprised to find some pods with only round seeds. Mendel had a mind for mathematics, and he

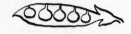
Strain with Round Peas  Strain with Wrinkled Peas

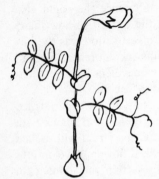

The Parents

The Children or
1st Generation Hybrids

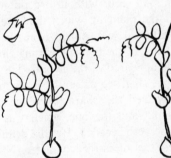

Some of the Children Grown Up

Some of the Grandchildren or 2nd Generation Hybrids

FIG. 1.
One of Mendel's experiments.

was struck by the fact that 5,474 is nearly three times as many as 1,850. He was even more impressed when he found that all seven pairs of contrasting characters which he combined by crossing gave the same result: always one of the two characters was dominant and showed in all first-generation hybrids, while the other was recessive and reappeared in one third of the second-generation hybrids.

From these experiments Mendel developed a theory of heredity, according to which the material basis of heredity consists of "factors," which are carried singly in the germ cells, combine in pairs at fertilization and separate again when the next generation forms germ cells. This theory was so far ahead of what was then known about cell structure and fertilization that modern geneticists stand amazed at the brilliance of a mind which, starting from very simple observations, could push so far, so confidently, and so daringly into completely unexplored territories. It is not surprising that the first fate of Mendel's discovery was complete neglect by contemporary scientists. Only after Mendel's death, in 1900, was his theory "rediscovered" simultaneously through the observations of three botanists working in three different European countries. By then cytology, that is, the microscopical study of the cell, had advanced to a stage where Mendel's factors could soon be correlated with the most striking cellular structure, the chromosomes. Instead of trying to follow Mendel's brilliant deductions, we shall choose the easy road of deriving his laws of heredity from the observed behavior of the chromosomes.

CHAPTER 3   *The Chromosomes*

ALL LIVING ORGANISMS consist of cells. Bacteria and many primitive "microorganisms" consist of single cells; higher organisms are composed of vast numbers of cells. With rare exceptions, cells are exceedingly small and cannot be seen without the help of a microscope. Plate II, 1, shows a plant cell at several hundred times magnification. It is filled with a living substance called cytoplasm. Suspended in the cytoplasm you see a more compact body; this is the nucleus. Every cell contains a nucleus, and although cells may survive for quite a while without nucleus, they can no longer divide. In cells treated with certain dyes, the nucleus shows a network of stained material and usually also one or a few more densely stained clumps. This is all that can be seen of the chromosomes at this stage. When a cell divides, the membrane surrounding the nucleus breaks down and the chromosomes come out into the cytoplasm. They have now contracted into rod-shaped structures which in many cells can be seen during life and without staining, but are most clearly observed in stained cells. It is their ability to take up certain dyes which has given them their name (chromosome-stained body). Plate II, 2, shows the stained chromosomes in a dividing cell of the broad bean plant, Vicia faba. You can easily count that there are 12 of them, and you can also see that they differ from each other in size and shape. If you would look at more Vicia cells you would find that every one of them contains the same 12 chromosomes. Similarly, every cell of a pea plant contains 14 chromosomes; every cell of the fruit fly Drosophila melanogaster

14

contains 8 chromosomes (Plate II, 3), every cell of a mouse contains 40 chromosomes (Plate II, 4), and every human cell 46 chromosomes (Plate II, 6). In general, number, sizes and shapes of chromosomes are characteristics of each species.

How is it brought about that every cell of an individual receives the same chromosome outfit? New cells arise through division of old ones. In preparation for cell division, every chromosome makes another chromosome exactly like itself. At first these two chromosomes, the old one and the new one, lie close together; but when the cell divides they separate and each of the two sister cells receives one copy of each chromosome. The intricate mechanism by which this distribution of sister chromosomes into sister cells is achieved is called mitosis. Since its details have no bearing on Mendel's laws, we shall not consder them here; you will find them described in almost every textbook of biology. For us it is sufficient to bear in mind that, as a result of chromosome replication and mitosis, the same chromosomes are present in every cell of every organism of a given species. There is one important exception to this rule, and with this we shall deal now. It will take us right up to the point where genetics joins hand with cytology, the study of the cell.

Let us turn once more to the photographs on Plate II. If you look at cells with few chromosomes (Vicia, 2; Drosophila, 3) you will notice that these can be arranged into pairs. Every chromosome that stands out by its size and shape can be matched by another one of the same kind. Thus in Drosophila, we find one pair of medium-sized chromosomes, two pairs of long ones, and one pair of very small, dot-like chromosomes. In cells with many small chromosomes the arrangement into pairs may not be obvious. Plate II, 7, shows how the 46 human chromosomes (Plate II, 6) can be arranged fairly convincingly into pairs by cutting out the photographs of all individual chromosomes and matching them according to size and shape. Even where such attempts are not successful we can feel quite confident that the chromosomes can be arranged into pairs, because in the life cycle of every sexually reproducing organism there occurs a stage when the chromosomes do the pairing off themselves. This stage is called meiosis, which signifies diminution; we shall see presently why this term was chosen.

Meiosis is a sequence of two cell divisions which follow closely on each other; it is the first step in the formation of the mature germ cells or gametes. Fig. 2 is a grossly oversimplified diagram of meiosis for one pair of chromosomes; it shows only those features that are relevant for an understanding of Mendel's laws. Details can be found in many textbooks of biology. At the beginning of meiosis partner chromosomes come together and wind around each other in various ways. Plate II, 8, shows this for the 14 chromosomes of rye, which in meiosis form 7 pairs. As in many old dances,

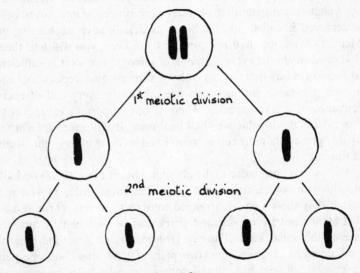

FIG. 2.
Meiosis for one pair of chromosomes.

pairing of partners is the prelude to their moving apart. At the end of the first meiotic division, all pairs have dissolved, and the partners have moved separately into the two sister cells. Again, as in mitosis, division has resulted in an equal distribution of chromosomes into sister cells, but there is an all-important difference. In mitosis, each cell receives the full complement of chromosomes; in meiosis it receives only one member of each chromosome pair. Thus, the first meiotic division reduces the chromosome number to half; it is therefore called the reduction division. The second meiotic division is an ordinary mitosis and does not produce any more changes in chromosome number. The final outcome of the two meiotic divisions is a group of four germ cells, each of which contains one "set" of chromosomes, that is, one member of each chromosome pair. Such a cell is called "haploid," while cells with two matching chromosome sets are called "diploid." Expressed in these terms, meiosis produces four haploid germ cells from one diploid mother cell. Plate II, 5, is a photo of the chromosomes in an ovum (egg) of the mouse; you may count that there are 20 of them, half as many as in an ordinary body cell of the mouse (Plate II, 4). At fertilization two gametes, each carrying one set of chromosomes, come together and restore the diploid condition. The circle is closed, and a new circle will start when the next generation forms its germ cells.

CHAPTER 4   *The Genes*

LET US TURN BACK to Mendel's experiments. You may already have noticed the remarkable parallelism between the behavior of Mendel's hypothetical hereditary factors and the behavior of the not-at-all hypothetical chromosomes. Like the chromosomes, the factors are carried singly in mature germ cells. Like the chromosomes, they come together in pairs at fertilization. Like the chromosomes, they separate, or "segregate," again when the next generation forms its germ cells. There is only one objection to regarding the chromosomes as Mendelian factors: there are much too few of them. A pea plant, for example, has seven pairs of chromosomes. Mendel studied seven pairs of contrasting characters, and it is evident that he might have studied many more. In order to account, in terms of separate factors, for the hereditary constitution of a complex organism like a pea plant, a fly, a mouse, a human being, tens of thousands of factors have to be postulated. The way out of this dilemma consists of considering the chromosomes not as the hereditary factors themselves, but as the vehicles on which these factors are carried from generation to generation. The truth of this assumption has been borne out by innumerable experiments, and there can no longer be any doubt that the hereditary factors, or "genes," are aligned along the chromosomes, each chromosome carrying hundreds or thousands of them.

The genes are much too small to be seen individually, but in certain stages many chromosomes show lengthwise patterns of knobs or bands that indicate their subdivision into genes. In particular, this happens during the early stages of meiosis. Plate III, 1, shows a pair of rye chromosomes at the beginning of meiosis. You notice the pattern of darkly stained knobs and faintly stained connecting strands. The pattern in the two partner chromosomes is the same, and pairing is exceedingly accurate, each knob in one chromosome lying next to the matching knob in its partner. It appears that it is the genes rather than the chromosomes as a whole that direct the pairing process. This ability of the genes to find and attract their exact counterparts is one of their many remarkable properties for which science has not yet found a satisfactory explanation. Later on in meiosis the pattern will be lost because the chromosomes curl up and contract into the compact bodies you saw in Plate II, 8. But when the next generation makes germ cells, each chromosome will again show its characteristic pattern, so that a trained cytologist can recognize every one of the seven chromosomes of rye by the pattern of its knobs.

Giant chromosomes with beautiful and intricate patterns of dark and light bands are found in the salivary glands of the larvae (maggots) of certain flies. Plate III, 2, shows such chromosomes in the salivary glands of Drosophila larvae. They are hundreds of times as long as ordinary chromosomes, and each of them has its own characteristic pattern of bands. They are also much thicker than ordinary chromosomes because each consists of a bundle of many strands, all with exactly the same pattern of bands. The way these bundles arise is interesting because it illustrates the extreme accuracy of chromosome replication. In the young larva, the chromosomes in the salivary glands are still thin. As the larva grows, the salivary glands grow too, but they do so in a particular way. The cells, instead of making more cells by division, grow bigger and bigger without division. Their nuclei, too, grow bigger and bigger. Inside the nuclei, the chromosomes make replicas of themselves as they do in preparation for mitosis but, as there is no mitosis, the new chromosomes do not separate from the old ones. Instead, new and old chromosomes remain closely attached to each other and each, in turn, makes more replicas. This goes on repeatedly, and so accurately does each band make another band like itself that the whole bundle appears as one single thick banded thread. In addition, the partner chromosomes in the salivary glands are closely paired as in meiosis, so that each apparent chromosome represents one pair, and the nuclei of the salivary glands of Drosophila seem to have four chromosomes instead of the eight that are visible in ordinary cells (Plate II, 3). The pattern of bands corresponds to the pattern of underlying genes. This can often be seen in cases where a chromosome has lost a small piece through radiation or some other injury. The accuracy of chromosome replication is such that all descendants of the damaged chromosome lack exactly the same piece, and when such a damaged chromosome gets into a gamete, for instance an ovum, individuals are formed which lack the same

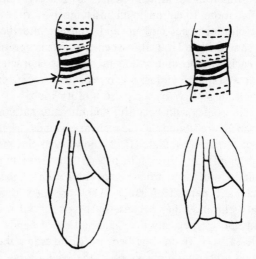

FIG. 3.
Deficiency for a wing gene in Drosophila.

chromosome piece in all their cells. Figures 3 and 4 illustrate what may happen in such cases.

The left part of Figure 3 shows a normal wing of Drosophila and above it, and at a very much higher magnification, a little section of one of the normal salivary gland chromosomes. The arrow points to a band which encloses a gene for wing shape. The right part of Figure 3 shows the same chromosome section in a fly which had received a damaged chromosome from its X-rayed father or mother. If you recall that the salivary gland chromosomes consist of two chromosome bundles formed by the two partner chromosomes, you will understand why only half a band is missing at the point of the arrow. Nevertheless, the lack of one of the two partner genes has been sufficient to disturb normal development of the wing and to produce the abnormal shape shown in the accompanying sketch. Flies which have lost this band from both partner chromosomes are so much damaged that they die as early embryos.

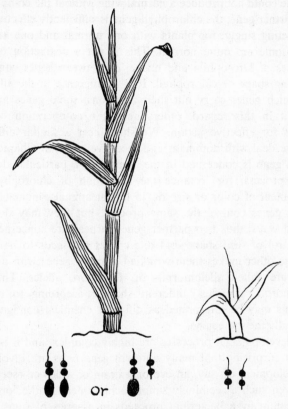

FIG. 4.
Deficiency for a chlorophyll gene in maize.

A similar case is shown in Figure 4. The left drawing represents a normally growing green maize plant and underneath, at much higher magnification, the tips of one particular chromosome pair. There is a fairly large knob at the end of these chromosomes. Among the genes which this knob encloses is one whose action is necessary for the production of the green substance chlorophyll that is essential for survival of the plant. The right picture shows that, when this knob has been lost from both chromosomes, the plant dies early as a yellow and sickly seedling. If you turn once more to the left picture you will notice a striking difference from what happened in the case of the Drosophila wing gene. Whereas this gene could not produce a normal wing without the co-operation of its partner gene, the chlorophyll gene is sufficiently effective even when acting singly; for plants with one normal and one knobless chromosome are quite normal. This is not a distinction between the genes of Drosophila and maize, or between genes concerned with wing shape or chlorophyll. It is a difference in the efficiency with which genes carry out their functions; some genes are self-sufficient in this regard, others need the co-operation of their partners for effective action. We shall meet a similar difference when we deal with dominant and recessive genes in Chapter 6.

Each gene is concerned in the control of a particular developmental process, for instance the formation of chlorophyll, the development of color or size or, in higher animals, mental ability. Partner genes control the same process, but they may do so in different ways; thus two partner genes in peas are concerned with the control of seed shape, but one causes the seeds to be round, while the other makes them wrinkled. Partner genes with different effects are called allelomorphs or, for short, alleles. The term "allelomorph" signifies "different shape"; according to modern ideas this may be interpreted as different chemical configurations of basically the same gene.

All developmental processes are highly complex, and it is therefore not surprising that many different gene pairs are involved in the development of, say, an eye or a brain or a flower (see Chap. 23). Even such a seemingly simple achievement as the formation of a vitamin by a bacterium proceeds in a series of steps and is controlled by a series of genes. In bacteria, genes controlling the same process tend to lie close together, as though this facilitated their co-operation; but in most other organisms this is not found to be so. Genes which are involved in quite different processes may lie cheek by jowl on the same chromosome, while genes controlling closely related processes may lie far apart. Figure 5 shows the position of a few of the known genes on a particular pair of chromosomes of the fruit fly Drosophila melanogaster. Only genes

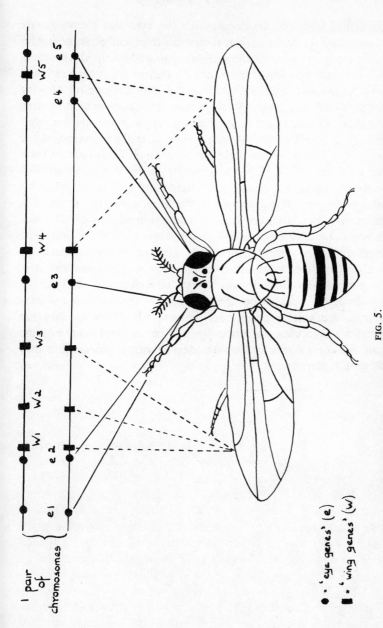

● = 'eye genes' (e)

■ = 'wing genes' (w)

FIG. 5.

The positions of some wing and eye genes on one of the chromosomes of Drosophila.

concerned with the development of the eyes and the wings are represented; more genes controlling development of these organs are present on the same chromosome pair and on the three others. Some of the represented genes can be seen to act in very different ways; thus wing gene w1 is concerned with the control of wing shape, while wing gene w2 helps make the correct pattern of wing venation. For other genes such a distinction is not evident; thus eye genes e1, e2, e3 and e4 are all engaged in the formation of eye color. Yet we know from developmental studies that each of them has a different role to play in this process.

Before going on to the next chapter, it will be useful if we summarize what this chapter has taught us about the genes. The genes, like the chromosomes, are arranged in pairs; with the chromosomes they segregate into different gametes at meiosis and come together again at fertilization, one member of each pair being derived from the father, one from the mother. The arrangement of the genes on the chromosomes is fixed for each species, and partner genes occupy identical positions on partner chromosomes. Allelomorphs are partner genes with different effect, that is, they are genes which occupy the same position on the same chromosome pair and control exactly the same developmental process, but they do so in different ways.

CHAPTER 5   *Mendel's First Law: Segregation*

AFTER THIS EXCURSION into cytology, let us return to genetics. The chief tool of the cytologist is the microscope; it has shown him that the chromosomes, and with them the genes, segregate at meiosis and enter the gametes singly. The chief tool of the geneticist is the crossing of different strains, and we are now going to consider crosses which demonstrate the segregation of the genes at meiosis. It will be useful for the description of these experiments if we recall some technical terms which have already been defined, namely "haploid" and "diploid" for cells or individuals which carry one or two chromosome sets, respectively, and "allelomorphs" or "alleles" for partner genes with different effects. To these terms I want to add two new ones which describe the genetical constitution of a diploid individual in regard to any particular pair of genes. Evidently there exist two possibilities: either the partner genes are alike or they are allelomorphic. In the first case, the individual is "homozygous" or a "homozygote" in respect to the gene concerned; in the second case, it is called "heterozygous" or a "heterozygote." A pea plant with two genes for wrinkled seeds or two genes for round seeds is homozygous for either wrinkled or round; a pea plant with one gene for wrinkled seed and an allelomorphic gene for round seed is heterozygous for wrinkled and round. It will readily be seen that only heterozygotes are suitable for demonstrating the segregation of genes; for the geneticist recognizes genes by their effects, and the segregation of like genes in a homozygote is not observable.

In higher organisms (macroorganisms) it is hardly ever possible to observe the immediate effects of segregation at meiosis; for the mature gametes fuse at fertilization and the progeny, in which we

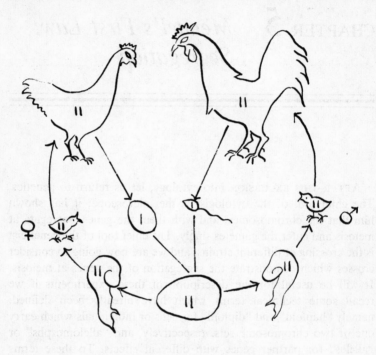

I = haploid

II = diploid

FIG. 6.
Life cycle of fowl.

observe the effects of the genes, carries genes from two different gametes. Figure 6 shows the life cycle of the domestic fowl in terms of haploidy and diploidy. The diploid female and male form haploid ova and spermatozoa. At fertilization the gametes fuse and form the fertilized ovum, which in turn develops into the diploid embryo, chicken and adult. Thus the whole life cycle, with the exception of one cell generation, is spent in the diploid stage.

The situation is quite different for many microorganisms. Figure 7 shows the life cycle of a green alga, Chlamydomonas. Each individual of this species is a microscopically small cell which swims through the water with the aid of two whiplike hairs, or "flagellae." These cells are haploid; they have only one set of chromosomes, carrying all genes of the species in single copies. New cells are formed through division of the old ones. In this way whole popu-

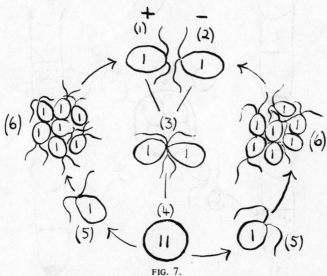

FIG. 7.
Life cycle of the microscopic alga Chlamydomonas.

lations (6) may be derived from one cell (5) by repeated divisions. Such populations are called "clones." Since at mitosis both daughter cells receive exactly the same set of chromosomes and genes (p. 15), all cells within a clone are genetically identical. There are no visibly distinct sexes, but physiologically there is a clear distinction between sexes or "mating types," called + and − in our diagram. Cells of the same clone are always of the same mating type and never mate with each other; nor does mating occur when cells of two + clones or two − clones are brought together. But when cells from a + and a − strain are put into the same culture vessel, pairs are formed. Each pair [(1) and (2)] consists of one + and one — cell; they fuse (3) and form a thick-skinned spore called a zygote (4). The zygote is comparable to a fertilized ovum in, say, a dog or a fly. It contains the chromosomes from both gametes and is, therefore, diploid. Very soon after fertilization meiosis takes place inside the zygote, and haploid gametes (5)

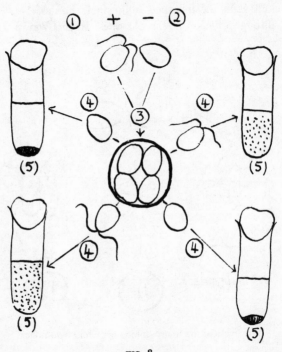

FIG. 8.
Segregation for absence of flagellae in Chlamydomonas. Cells without flagellae cannot swim and sink to the bottom of the culture vessel.

swarm out. These start a new life cycle by division; in fact, the gametes of Chlamydomonas do not differ from any of the other free-swimming cells. Thus in this alga, as in many other micro-organisms, the whole life cycle, with the exception of the zygote, takes place in the haploid stage, and segregation at meiosis is not obscured by diploidy of the progeny.

Usually it is necessary to grow the gametes into clones before segregation becomes observable; but occasionally the segregating gametes themselves differ visibly from each other. Figure 8 illustrates such a case in Chlamydomonas. Two strains (1) and (2) differ in one gene which is concerned with the development of the flagellae. While strain (1) has all the genes necessary for flagella formation, strain (2) carries a deficient allele of one of these genes and cannot, therefore, develop flagellae. When the two strains are crossed by bringing together + cells from the one strain with − cells from the other (it makes no difference which strain provides the + cells, which the − cells), a zygote (3) is formed which carries both alleles and is, thus, heterozygous for the gene in question. At the reduction division the partner chromosomes segregate and carry the different alleles into separate cells. At the second meiotic division each cell divides once more by mitosis, so that finally four gametes are formed, two of which carry the normal and two the deficient allele. When these swarm out (4), it will be seen immediately that two have flagellae, two have not. This difference persists in the clones formed from the gametes. If we let each gamete grow into a separate clone (5), two clones will consist of flagellated free-moving cells, while two will consist of flagellaless cells which sink to the bottom of the tube.

The fact that a heterozygous zygote always produces two gametes carrying one allele and two carrying the other is so well established that it can be used, conversely, for determining whether a difference between two strains of a microorganism is due to the effects of a pair of allelomorphic genes. If this is so, the gametes from a cross between the strains will yield two clones, resembling the one strain, and two resembling the other. Figure 9 illustrates an experiment in which this method was used for the genetical analysis of a biochemical property of yeast. Yeast, like Chlamydomonas, is a unicellular (one-celled) organism. Many strains are haploid and can be used in experiments on segregation. Like Chlamydomonas, yeast occurs in two mating types, + and −, which are not visibly different from each other. Yeast, as you know, ferments sugar into alcohol and carbon dioxide gas; but strains differ in their ability to ferment various kinds of sugar. Thus some strains readily ferment galactose (one of the components of milk sugar), while others do so only very slowly and inefficiently. A simple method for detecting fermentation is to catch the developing gas

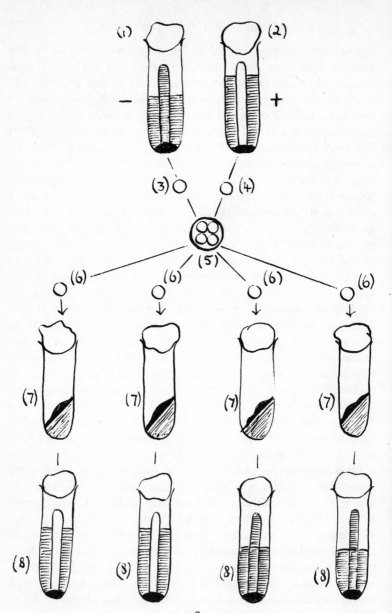

FIG. 9.
Segregation in yeast for the ability to ferment galactose. The cultures in the center row are grown on solid medium with glucose. The cultures in the top and bottom rows are grown in liquid medium with galactose as only sugar. In liquid medium, cells that can ferment galactose fill the inner tube with carbon dioxide gas.

in a test tube which was first completely filled with liquid and then inserted immediately above the yeast cells. If the medium contains a sugar which can be fermented, the tube gradually fills with gas; if the sugar cannot be fermented, the tube remains filled with liquid. In the experiment shown in Fig. 9 the medium in the top row contains galactose as the only sugar. Strain (2) is able to ferment this sugar, strain (1) is not. Cells (3) and (4) from the two strains are brought together, and a zygote (5) is formed which, through meiosis, gives rise to four gametes (6). Each gamete is grown into a clone (7) on solid medium containing glucose, a sugar which can be fermented by all strains of yeast. Finally, the four clones are tested (8) in fermentation tubes with galactose as the only sugar. You will notice that two clones (those on the left) can ferment galactose, and two cannot. Thus the difference between the two original parents segregates in the 2:2 (or 1:1) ratio expected if it is due to the action of a single gene pair. On the basis of several experiments of this kind it could be concluded that in yeast the ability to ferment galactose is controlled by the action of a gene which in nonfermenting strains is absent, or is present in the form of a nonfunctioning or poorly functioning allelomorph.

The facts discussed in this chapter form the essence of what is called Mendel's first law or the law of segregation. In modern terms it may be expressed as follows:

When a heterozygote forms gametes, half of them carry one of the two alleles, half the other. The basis for the segregation of the genes is the segregation of the chromosomes at meiosis.

Mendel himself could not, of course, interpret his results in these terms, but he quite clearly postulated that a mechanism of this kind was responsible for his data, in particular for the famous and much overrated 3:1 ratio. This particular ratio is a rather remote consequence of the underlying gametic segregation in a ratio of 1:1. In the next chapter we shall follow the steps by which, in crosses between higher organisms, this 1:1 ratio becomes transformed into others, including 3:1. In doing this we shall find ourselves using very simple statistical rules, such as are used for predicting that a coin tossed 100 times will show head about 50 times. This statistical aspect of genetics has been held against it by the Lysenko school, on the grounds that mathematics must not be applied to biological objects and that Mendel had no right to speak of a 3:1

ratio between round and wrinkled peas if some of the pods contained 6 round peas. No matter what we think about these arguments—and to a modern biologist they seem entirely futile—I want to stress that the basic rule of segregation is *not* statistical. Wherever it is possible to study segregation directly in the four products of meiosis, *exactly* two are of one kind and two of the other.

CHAPTER 6 *A Very Little Statistics*

WE SHALL NOW INTRODUCE a distinction which is fundamental to genetics: the distinction between "phenotype" and "genotype." By phenotype we understand the appearance of an organism, using the term "appearance" in its widest sense. Thus the phenotype of a bacterium is not only its shape and size but also its ability to cause disease, its resistance or sensitivity to drugs, its rate of multiplication, the nutrients it requires, etc. The phenotype of a man includes thousands of characteristics of body and mind: his stature, his pulse rate, his social attitude, his intelligence quotient—to name a few of them at random. By genotype we understand the total gene outfit of an organism, including the way the genes are arranged on the chromosomes. To describe exhaustively the phenotype of an organism may be too demanding of time and effort to be a practical proposition, but in theory it could be done. To describe exhaustively the genotype of even the simplest organism is impossible because every genotype contains many genes whose very existence is unknown to us. When a gene does not occur in several allelomorphic forms we do not and cannot know that it exists. We know, e.g., that cattle possess genes which determine whether or not horns will be formed; for in crosses between horned and hornless breeds we find that these contrasting characters segregate in the progeny. We may presume that cattle also possess genes which determine whether or not a heart will be formed; but since we cannot cross animals with and without heart, the existence of these genes remains pure surmise. Similarly, in Chlamydomonas the existence of a gene that controls formation of the flagellae could be inferred only after individuals without flagellae had become available for crosses. Even in the genetically best-analyzed organisms, such as Drosophila or maize, we know only a small fraction of all the genes.

In practice we are never concerned with either the phenotype or the genotype as a whole. In the simplest cases we limit ourselves to the phenotypical effects of individual genes, for example to the pair of allelomorphic genes which, in Chlamydomonas, determines whether or not a flagella will be formed, or to the pair of allelomorphs which, in the pea, determines whether the seeds will be round or wrinkled. Here the phenotype is always immediately apparent; but while in the haploid Chlamydomonas the genotype may be inferred directly from the phenotype, this is not so in the diploid pea plant. For in diploids we are confronted with a complication which Mendel described as "dominance" versus "recessivity" (p. 11), and which we now shall discuss in terms of gene effects.

A diploid organism, as we saw, can be heterozygous or homozygous in regard to any pair of genes (p. 25). A pea plant, e.g., may be homozygous for the "round" gene, homozygous for the "wrinkled" gene, or heterozygous, carrying the "round" gene on one chromosome and the "wrinkled" gene in the corresponding position on the partner chromosome. (The descriptive terms have been set in quotation marks because they obviously refer to the shape of the seeds and not to that of the genes. In the diagram we have, however, represented the genes as though they, themselves, showed the shapes which they produce in the seeds.) Figure 10 shows the phenotypes corresponding to the three possible genotypes for seed shape. It is evident that homozygotes for the "wrinkled" gene will have wrinkled seeds and homozygotes for the "round" gene will have "round" seeds. But it is not evident what the phenotype of the heterozygote will be. This is decided by the relative efficiencies of the two alleles in influencing development and has to be found out by observation. In the present case, the "round" gene is the more efficient partner, so much so that the heterozygote is phenotypically indistinguishable from the homozygote for the "round" gene. Adopting Mendel's terminology, we call the round gene "dominant" and the wrinkled gene "recessive."

These two terms are relative terms, referring to pairs of alleles; they make no sense when applied to an individual gene. Just as John may be stronger than Bill, but weaker than Jim, so a gene may be dominant in relation to one allele and recessive in relation to another. As a general definition we may say that gene *A* is called dominant over its recessive allele *a* when the phenotype of the heterozygote *Aa* is determined by *A* to the exclusion of gene *a*. (This definition makes use of the convention to denote alleles

Genotype

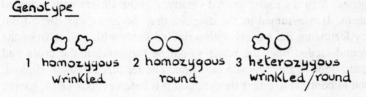

1 homozygous wrinkled   2 homozygous round   3 heterozygous wrinkled/round

Phenotype

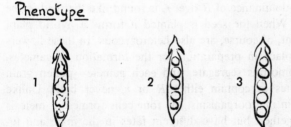

1   2   3

FIG. 10.
Dominance of round over wrinkled seed in peas.

by the same letter, using a capital letter for the dominant member of a pair, and a small letter for the recessive member.)

Looking once again at Fig. 10 you will easily realize that dominance is a factor which may mask the genotype in the phenotype; for phenotypically the seeds of plants (2) and (3) are indistinguishable, although genotypically they are different. We shall see presently how this difficulty may be overcome in cases where it is important to know the genotype of an organism. But first let us end this long detour through cytology and modern genetics by explaining, in terms of dominant and recessive genes, how Mendel obtained his 3:1 ratio.

You will recall (or will do so by looking at Fig. 1) that a cross between round-seeded and wrinkled-seeded pea plants produced hybrid seeds which were all round, but that the plants grown from these seeds produced round and wrinkled seeds in a ratio of 3 round to 1 wrinkled. Figure 11 pictures this experiment once more, this time with the addition of the genotypes. *R* denotes the gene for round seeds, *r* the gene for wrinkled seeds. The parent plants are diploid and homozygous for either the *R* gene (*RR*) or the *r* gene (*rr*). Their gametes are haploid and carry one of the two genes: *R* in the round-seeded variety, *r* in the variety with wrinkled seeds. It is assumed in the diagram that the cross was carried out by fertilizing the variety with wrinkled seeds with pollen from the round-seeded one; the result would be the same if the cross had been done in the opposite direction. The fertilized ovule is diploid, but in contrast to either parent plant it is heterozygous (*Rr*), having received an *R* gene through the pollen in addition to its own *r* gene. The ovule develops into the heterozygous or (hybrid) seed which, because of the dominance of *R* over *r,* is round like the seed in the pollen parent. When the seed is planted it forms a hybrid plant with flowers that, of course, are also heterozygous. In these flowers meiosis takes place in preparation for the formation of gametes. The two allelomorphs segregate, and each gamete—pollen grain or ovule—comes to contain either *R* or *r,* never both. Unlike what happens in microorganisms, the four cells formed at meiosis do not stay together, but have different fates in the male and female organs. The pollen grains become thoroughly mixed, and large numbers compete for fertilization of the available ovules. The ovules develop from only one cell in each cluster of four, while the other three cells degenerate. This, incidentally, is the usual history of female gametes in higher organisms; it arises from the necessity for providing sufficient nourishment for the embryo that will develop from the fertilized ovum. What, we may well ask, has become of the beautifully simple 2:2 or 1:1 segregation under these conditions? The answer is that it has been preserved, but as a statistical rather than an accurate ratio. It is easy to see why this is so. Consider first the male germ cells, that is, the pollen grains in plants, the spermatozoa in animals. Originally they occur in bundles of four, each bundle consisting of exactly two of one type, two of the other. If a large number of such bundles is mixed,

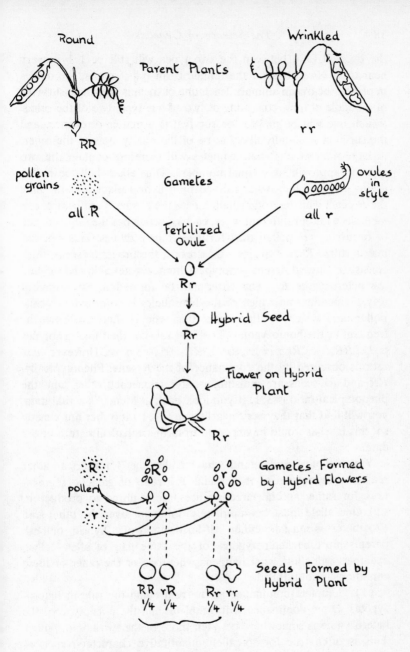

FIG. 11.
Mendel's experiment (Fig. 1) explained. The 3:1 ratio.

the over-all ratio between the two types will still be 1:1 or very near to it. Now consider the female germ cells, that is, the ovules in plants, the ova in animals. Each one of them is the single survivor of a bundle of four, consisting of two of one type, two of the other. Which one will be picked for survival is a matter of chance, and the survivor is equally likely to be of the one type as of the other. A large number of female gametes will therefore contain the two types in approximately equal numbers. Thus about half the pollen grains and half the ovules formed by a hybrid plant *Rr* will carry the *R* gene, while the other half carries the *r* gene. Fertilization can take place in four different ways, each of which has the same chance of occurring: *R* pollen may fertilize *R* or *r* ovules, and *r* pollen may fertilize *R* or *r* ovules. As a result, the progeny (seeds) will consist of three different genotypes: homozygotes *RR* and *rr,* and the heterozygote *Rr*. The latter can be formed in two different ways, depending on which of the two alleles is contributed by the pollen and which by the ovule; this type is therefore twice as frequent as the homozygotes. The final ratio of the three genotypes is ¼ *RR* : ½ *Rr* : ¼ *rr,* or 1 *RR* : 2 *Rr* : 1 *rr*. However, this ratio is obscured by the dominance of the *R* gene. Phenotypically, *RR* and *Rr* seeds are indistinguishable from each other, and the phenotypical ratio is 3:1. If you look back at Mendel's actual data, you will find that they very nearly give a 3:1 ratio, but not exactly so; this is what would be expected from the statistical nature of the data.

You will now understand why I called the 3:1 ratio a rather remote consequence of the crucial 1:1 ratio of gametic segregation, for rather special circumstances are required to produce it. (1) One allele must be completely dominant over the other and (2) the cross must be either self-fertilization of a hybrid, or both parents must be heterozygous for the same pair of alleles. Two examples will show what happens when one or the other of these conditions is not fulfilled:

(1) Complete dominance is far from being the rule in heterozygotes. Often dominance is incomplete, and the phenotype of the heterozygote is somewhere between those of the two homozygotes. This is often true for so-called quantitative characters, such as stature or weight; but also qualitative characters, such as presence or absence of color, may show incomplete dominance. In Short-

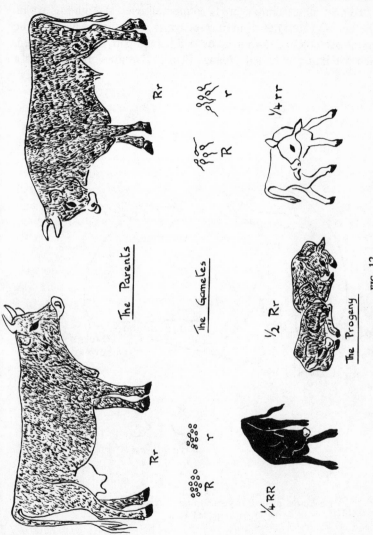

The Parents

Rr   Rr

The Gametes

R r   R r

The Progeny

¼ RR   ½ Rr   ¼ rr

FIG. 12.

The inheritance of roan color in Shorthorn cattle. The 1:2:1 ratio.

horn cattle, a pair of alleles determines the amount of pigment in the coat. One homozygote is colored all over, the other is white. The heterozygote has a mixture of white and colored hairs; if the basic coat color, determined by a different pair of genes, is red, such a mixture is called "roan." Figure 12 shows the result of a

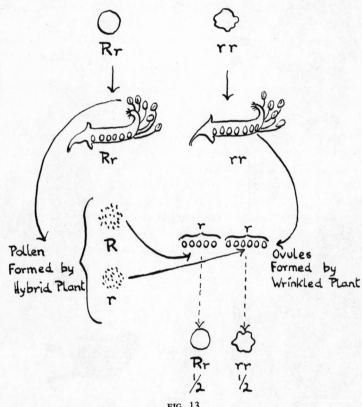

FIG. 13.
Backcross of heterozygous to homozygous recessive peas.
The 1:1 ratio.

mating between a roan bull and roan cows. The two alleles have been given the letters R and r, so that this cross can be compared more easily with the one shown in Fig. 11. The cross between two roan animals corresponds to self-fertilization of a hybrid pea plant, segregation into two classes of spermatozoa and ova corresponds to segregation into two classes of pollen and ovules, and the progeny consists of the three genotypes *RR, Rr,* and *rr* in the ratio 1:2:1. In the absence of dominance of one allele over the other, the phenotypical ratio is the same as the genotypical one, namely, ¼ red, ½ roan, and ¼ white calves. We cannot, of course, expect to find this ratio already realized among the first four or eight calves produced from such matings; but when data from many herds are pooled, they show very good agreement with it.

(2) Mendel, on the basis of his theory, predicted that all round seeds in the first generation and two thirds of those in the second should be hybrid or, as we would say now, heterozygous. In order to test this prediction he grew round seeds of both generations into plants and used the pollen of these plants for fertilizing plants which had grown from wrinkled seeds. All crosses carried out with first-generation hybrids and two thirds of those carried out with second-generation hybrids gave the expected result, which is illustrated in Fig. 13. The hybrid plants formed two types of pollen grain, *R* and *r,* in equal proportion, while the plants from wrinkled seeds formed only *r* ovules. Fertilization resulted in equal numbers of round and wrinkled seeds. This type of cross, in which a hybrid is crossed to one of the parental strains, is called a backcross. When, as in the present example, the parental strain is of the recessive type, the ratio of phenotypes in the progeny is the same as the segregation ratio of the gametes, namely, 1:1. This ratio and the backcross yielding it are much more important than the historical 3:1 ratio in a cross between two heterozygotes. Some applications of the backcross to animal breeding will be discussed in the next chapter.

CHAPTER 7 *Of Sheep, Mink and Dogs*

In 1791, on a farm in Massachusetts, a ewe gave rise to a very peculiar lamb with a long back and short, crooked legs. Although, on first being weaned, this lamb was less capable than the others of standing up to suckle, it developed into a healthy ram and sired several others like himself. These were the foundation animals of the otter, or Ancon, breed of sheep. Externally the animals were unprepossessing, so much so that Darwin called them "semimonstrous" and a chancellor of New York, who was also an expert on sheep, could write in 1809: "If a civilized nation, with whom taste has formed a standard for beauty, can consent to cripple God's works, and erect an altar to deformity, whereon to sacrifice the enjoyments of a helpless and useful animal, why should we be surprised that savages, ignorant of the beauty of proportion and the harmony of forms, should have early sought to curb the troublesome agility of their sheep, by giving the same preference to rickety tails that some among us have done to rickety legs?" This exasperated question already hints at the reason why New England farmers liked the breed in spite of its ugliness: Ancon sheep, because of their short legs, were unable to jump the low fences or stone walls with which the pastures were enclosed, and this prevented damage to cultivated land and meant saving in shepherds, dogs and hedges. The Ancon breed had been easy to build up and was easy to maintain. The original Ancon ram, when mated to his mother, sired more Ancons, and when these were crossed together they produced only Ancons. Subsequently, too, all matings between two Ancons resulted in nothing but Ancon lambs; on the other hand, normal parents might have an Ancon lamb, and when this had happened once, it was likely to happen again, although most lambs from such crosses were normal.

Darwin, in his book *Variation of Animals and Plants under Domestication* mentions the Ancon sheep as a rare instance of the sudden origin of a new breed. Although Mendel's fundamental paper had appeared several years before that book, Darwin never came to know of Mendel's work. If he had, it might have suggested to him a simple interpretation of the origin of the Ancon breed. While breeds in general differ from each other in many genes and consequently require many generations of selective breeding for their formation, the Ancon sheep differ from the original stock in only one gene which is responsible for their peculiar conformation. As illustrated in Fig. 14, I, this gene can be transmitted to lambs through outwardly normal parents which, therefore, must be heterozygous for it. By definition, a gene which remains hidden in a heterozygote is called "recessive." Being recessive, the Ancon gene becomes manifest only in homozygotes; thus, all Ancon sheep are homozygous and produce only Ancon lambs (Fig. 14, II).

This Mendelian explanation of the origin of the Ancon breed leaves unanswered the question of the origin of the Ancon gene. Why did no Ancon sheep occur prior to 1791, not even on the farm where subsequently two heterozygous parents did produce the first Ancon lamb? This is a difficult question to answer. We can, in fact, answer it only formally by giving a name to the rare and still incompletely understood process by which an old-established gene forms a new allelomorph. This process is called "mutation," and we shall have to say much more about it later on. For the present purpose it is sufficient to say that the Ancon gene happened to arise in this particular flock and at this particular time through mutation of one of the genes that, in sheep, control the development of the skeleton. As a matter of fact, we cannot at all be sure about the time of origin of the gene; for, being recessive, it may well have been carried hidden in several generations before the mating together of two heterozygotes produced the first Ancon lamb. A mutated gene, like its predecessor, makes new genes in its own image, and descendants of the first mutated gene were present in all Ancon sheep which, in New England, were bred

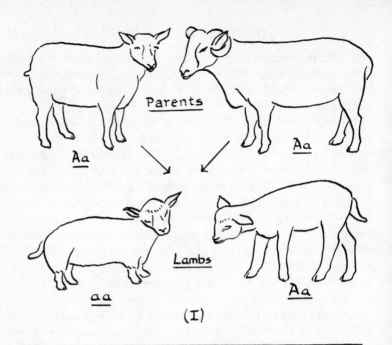

(I)

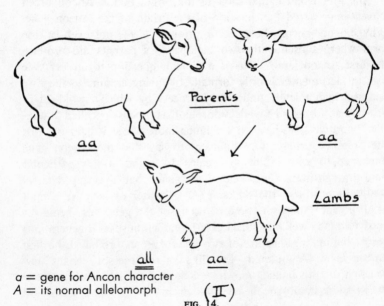

a = gene for Ancon character
A = its normal allelomorph

FIG. 14.

Inheritance of the Ancon character in sheep. Above: normal parents have produced one Ancon and one normal lamb. Below: Ancon parents produce only Ancon lambs.

until well into the second half of the nineteenth century. At the beginning of the present century, Ancon sheep turned up on a Norwegian farm; whether this European Ancon gene had been introduced into Norway in heterozygous breeding stock or whether it owed its origin to a new mutation is not known.

While it is rare for the agriculturist to use a single mutation for the foundation of a new breed, this is the rule for the fancier. Unlike the animal breeder whose interest centers round fertility, sturdiness, milk or egg yield or other characters which depend on the action of many genes, the fancier is interested in the outward appearance of his animals, and this may often be quite dramatically changed by the action of a single mutated (or "mutant") gene. Mink breeding furnishes good examples. The mink industry is still young. The first big mink shows were held in 1929 in the United States and in 1931 in Canada. The animals exhibited at these shows were extra-fine specimens of the dark type found wild in nature. In 1931 a mink rancher in Wisconsin found one light female kitten in an otherwise dark litter. When this female was crossed to a dark male, all the kittens were dark, but a backcross of one of the dark males to his mother produced more light-colored young. When animals of this type, now called "Silverblu" or "Platinum," were mated together all the kittens were like their parents, so that a true-breeding platinum strain was readily developed. The reader will realize that the history of the platinum mink is an almost exact repetition of the history of the Ancon sheep, and he will conclude correctly that platinum in mink, like Ancon in sheep, is due to a recessive gene which arose by mutation. Incidentally, a similar mutation occurred several years later at another mink ranch and was similarly made into a true-breeding strain. When animals of the two strains were crossed, the young were all platinum. To the geneticist this proved that the two mutations are identical. The reason for this may not be obvious to the reader; we shall come back to it in Chapter 22.

A breeder who wants to introduce the platinum mutation into his herd may do so by haphazard crosses, but he will achieve the same result with less loss of time and money if he applies Mendelian principles. The scheme of matings is illustrated in Fig. 15. The recessive platinum gene is denoted by p, its dark allele, present in the wild mink, by $+$. It is often convenient to use the $+$ sign for

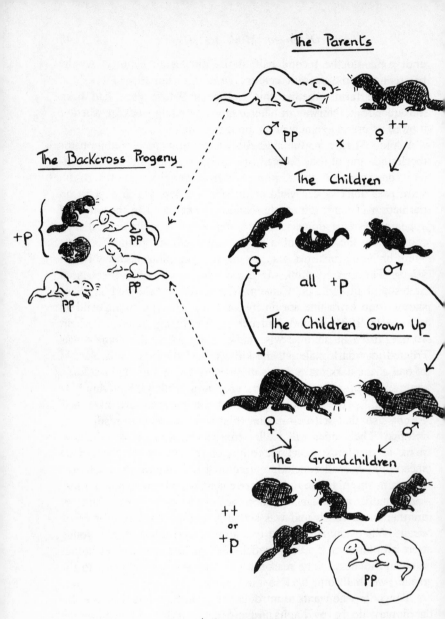

The Parents

The Backcross Progeny

♂ PP × ♀ ++

The Children

+p {

PP

PP

PP

all +p

The Children Grown Up

♀ ♂

♀ ♂

The Grandchildren

++
or
+p

PP

p = platinum gene
+ = its normal allelomorph

FIG. 15.
Inheritance of platinum fur in the mink.

genes present in the wild type. It may stand for either dominant or recessive genes. Obviously when, as here, the mutant gene is the recessive partner, the wild-type allele must be the dominant one. Thus platinum animals are genetically *pp*, wild-type animals are ++, and heterozygotes are +*p* and phenotypically dark like the wild type. When a platinum male (*pp*) is crossed with wild-type females (++) all the spermatozoa contain the *p* gene, all the ova the + gene, and all the offspring are +*p* and phenotypically dark. When they are crossed with each other, half the ova and half the spermatozoa carry the *p* gene, and about one quarter of the progeny will receive the gene through both sperm and ovum and will develop into platinum (*pp*) kittens. A better method for obtaining platinum kittens consists in crossing the original platinum male to his heterozygous (+*p*) daughters; for then all the spermatozoa and half the ova will carry the desired gene, and half the progeny will be platinum. Once platinum animals of both sexes have been obtained they can be used for establishing a true-breeding platinum strain.

Platinum was the first "mutation mink." It created a sensation on being exhibited at a fur auction sale in New York in 1944, where one dressed fur brought the top price of $265. Other mutations soon followed. One of the most famous—and most highly prized—ones is the black cross, or Koh-i-nur, shown in Fig. 16. The first black cross animal immediately had some black cross kittens among its progeny, and it was obvious to the geneticist that black cross, in contrast to platinum, must be a dominant mutation. It is, however, not completely dominant over its normal allele; for when Black Cross animals are mated together the kittens are of three types: dark, near-white, and black cross, the last-named class being about twice as frequent as either of the first two. The situation is exactly as in the roan cattle (Fig. 12). If we denote the mutant gene with *S*, its normal allele with +, then the heterozygote *S*+ is black cross, while the two homozygotes ++ and *SS* are dark and white respectively. One practical consequence of the incomplete dominance of *S* over + is that Koh-i-nur mink, like roan cattle, can never be obtained as a true-breeding strain. The breeder has the choice between litters which are mixed for Koh-i-nur and white (Fig. 16, I), Koh-i-nur and dark (Fig. 16, II), or all three types (Fig. 16, III).

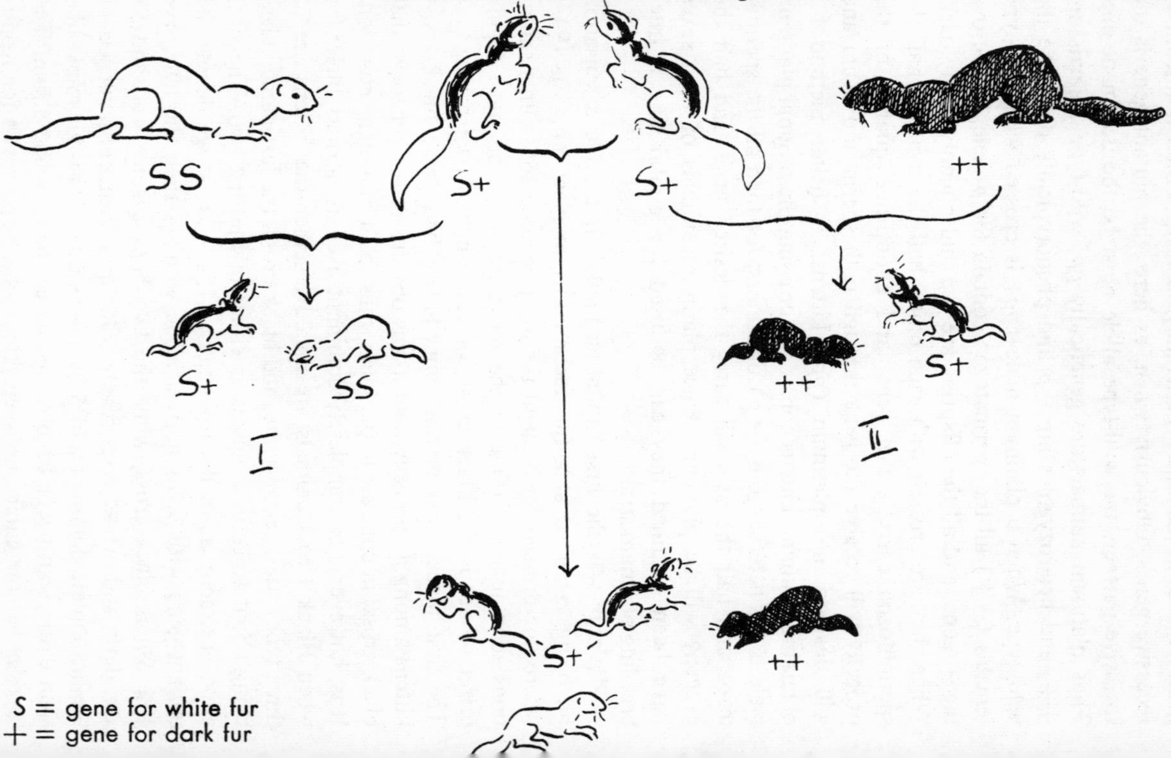
SS
S+
S+
++
S+
SS
I
++
S+
II
S+
++
S = gene for white fur
+ = gene for dark fur

FIG. 16.
Inheritance of Koh-i-nur fur in the mink. I. Koh-i-nur crossed with white. II. Koh-i-nur crossed with dark. III. Koh-i-nurs crossed together.

On the other hand, incomplete dominance has the advantage that the homozygote for the dominant type can be immediately distinguished from the heterozygote so that it is, for example, quite easy to build up a strain of true-breeding white minks by crossing whites (*SS*) with each other. This is not so for complete dominance where progeny tests may be necessary to distinguish the heterozygote from the dominant homozygote. In some breeds of

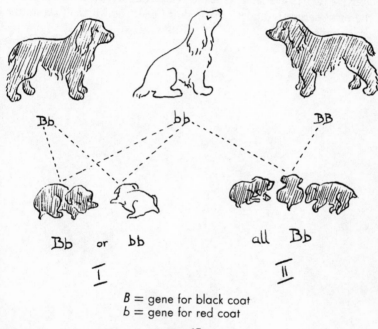

B = gene for black coat
b = gene for red coat

FIG. 17.
Progeny test of black dogs for the presence of a recessive gene for red coat color.

dogs, e.g., black coat color (*B*) is dominant over red (*b*), and if a mutation to red should crop up in a black strain it can spread through the kennels so that red pups (*bb*) crop up unexpectedly among the progeny of two black parents (*Bb*). A kennel owner who wants to get rid of the red gene can do so most efficiently by keeping some of the red animals as testers for the presence of the red gene in phenotypically black males or females (Fig. 17). When a heterozygote (*Bb*) is mated to such a red tester animal (*bb*), a red pup will appear sooner or later in the progeny. Homozygotes for black (*BB*) will yield nothing but black pups (*Bb*) in crosses with red, and black animals which in such crosses have produced six or seven black pups and no red ones can be used for reestablishing a true-breeding black strain.

These simple progeny tests for the presence of undesirable genes can be carried out whenever the recessive homozygote (red in the above case) is available as tester. Unfortunately, this is not so for the most seriously undesirable type of gene, as we shall see in the next chapter.

CHAPTER **8** *Genes That Kill*

In 1939, AT THE birthday celebrations of the American Legion in Paris, the Duchess of Windsor wore a magnificent stole made from an unusually light type of fox fur, called "platinum." Mutation to platinum had occurred several years previously at a Norwegian silver fox ranch, but the value of the new type was not immediately recognized. In 1937, however, at a fur auction in Norway, the new platinum furs brought up to $1000 for a set of two, and breeding animals were sold for as much as $6,000. None of these animals were true-breeding; when outcrossed to normal silver foxes they always produced silver as well as platinum young. The first mutant male, Mons, sired 3 silver and 4 platinum cubs, and the total progeny of the first Norwegian platinum foxes over three years consisted of 44 platinum and 41 silver young. Obviously, platinum in the fox, in contrast to platinum in the mink, is due to a dominant gene, which we may call *P*. Mons had received the mutated gene in one of the gametes which produced him; he was therefore heterozygous for this gene and for its normal allele (+). So were his offspring by silver females. Naturally the breeders were anxious to establish a true-breeding strain of this valuable variety. To this end they mated platinum males and females with each other. As expected, and as illustrated in Fig. 18, this always yielded some silver cubs in addition to platinum ones. However, some of the phenotypically platinum offspring— to be exact, 1 in every 3—should now be homozygous for the *P* gene and therefore suitable as foundation animals of a true-

51

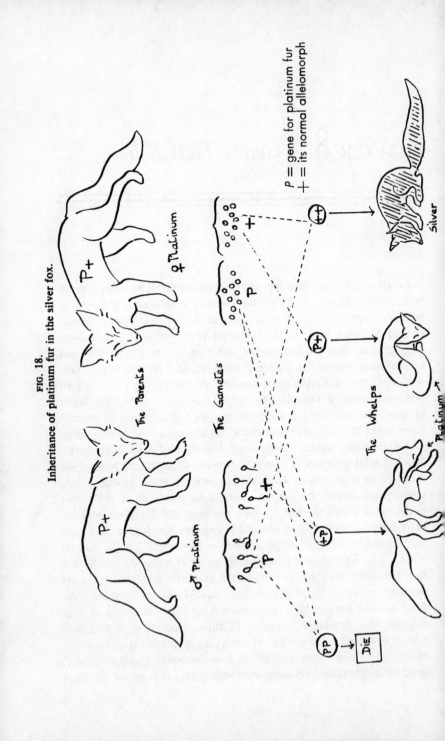

FIG. 18.
Inheritance of platinum fur in the silver fox.

P = gene for platinum fur
$+$ = its normal allelomorph

The Parents

The Gametes

The Whelps

Silver

Platinum

Platinum

$PP \rightarrow$ Die

breeding strain. Numerous progeny tests of the kind described on page 47 were carried out; but all tested animals disappointingly proved to be heterozygotes. At first this could be attributed to ill luck in choosing the platinum animals for progeny testing, but after a time it became obvious that the desired homozygotes simply did not exist. What could be the explanation? Mendel's first law is too well established to permit any doubt that homozygous *PP* embryos must be produced at fertilization; if, then, they do not appear among the progeny, it seems that they have died between fertilization and birth. If this is the correct interpretation, then litter size in matings of platinum to platinum should be smaller than normal, and this was indeed found to be true. While matings between silver and silver, or between silver and platinum, generally yield 4 or 5 whelps, those between platinum and platinum yielded only 3 or 4. Moreover, the ratio between platinum and silver whelps was not 3:1, as would be expected if all young survived, but 2:1 (127 platinum, 58 silver in 58 litters). A glance at Fig. 18 shows that this is the ratio expected if the *PP* homozygotes die during gestation. Breeders of platinum foxes must put up with smaller litter sizes and with the regular occurrence of about one third silver whelps among the platinum.

The effect of the platinum gene thus depends on whether it is present on both chromosomes or on only one of them. In the first case, the disturbance in development is so great that the embryo dies at an early stage. In the second, the effect is superficial, harmless to the animal, and attractive to man. In regard to the superficial effect, the gene is dominant, for heterozygotes are visibly mutant. In regard to the killing effect, the gene is recessive, for heterozygotes are perfectly healthy. Genes which kill the organism before it has completed development are called lethal genes. Platinum in the silver fox is a recessive lethal gene.

The lethal action of the platinum gene occurs so early that it has not yet been observed directly. Other lethal genes act late enough for their effects to be easily observable. The gene *T* in the laboratory mouse produces short and often twisted tails. All affected mice are heterozygotes $(T/+)$. When they are mated with normal mice, half the young are long-tailed, and half are short-tailed. Short-tailed mice mated with each other $(T/+ \times T/+)$ produce short-tailed and long-tailed young in a ratio of 2 : 1. Litter size is smaller than normal. During the first week of gestation, all embryos develop normally, but during the second week abnormalities begin to appear. The heterozygous embryos show defects in the tail region, the homozygous ones become grossly abnormal and die within a few days (Plate III, 3).

The platinum gene in silver foxes is maintained for economic reasons; the short-tail gene in laboratory mice is maintained for research purposes. If these genes ceased to be useful, it would be easy for the breeder to get rid of them, for they advertise their presence in heterozygotes by a visible effect. Unfortunately, most lethal genes in domestic animals are completely recessive and cannot be spotted in heterozygotes. This makes it difficult to get rid of them once they have appeared in a herd or flock. Moreover, they can spread widely before they are discovered through the accidental mating together of two heterozygotes.

Recessive lethals are known in most breeds of domestic animals. A gene causing dropsy is widespread in Ayrshire cattle. It kills calves at birth or soon afterward by accumulation of vast amounts of fluid in different parts of the body, especially head and limbs (Plate III, 4). Much worse from the breeder's point of view is the fact that a cow often dies when she gives birth to a dropsical calf. When the herdbooks were analyzed for the ancestors of dropsical calves it was found that many of these calves traced back to a few bulls which must have been heterozygous for the gene.

Occasionally it happens that an animal which carries a recessive harmful gene is used widely for breeding because of other desirable characters. Blindness became widespread in Irish setters during the 1930's, when nearly all the leading show dogs were descendants of one famous bitch, Rheona Didona, which was heterozygous for a gene causing atrophy of the retina. Under conditions of domestication, blindness is not lethal, and blind dogs, all of which are homozygous for the harmful gene (*bb*), can be used as tester animals. By culling all dogs or bitches which, in matings to a blind tester, produced one or more blind pups, the gene could be eliminated from the breed.

Toward the end of the nineteenth century, the Percheron stallion Superb was introduced from Ohio into Japan. Among his progeny in later generations there were many foals which died a few days after birth from an anatomical obstruction of the large intestine, caused by a recessive lethal gene. Superb must have carried this gene in heterozygous condition and inbreeding among his offspring resulted in homozygous foals. Two famous Holstein-Friesian bulls, Prinz Adolf and Gallus, introduced two recessive lethals, "hairless" and "amputated," into the Swedish Lowland breed. Hairless calves are born completely naked and die almost immediately; amputated calves are grossly malformed, with incomplete limbs and head (Plate III, 5). The usual test crosses are not possible in these cases because tester animals—that is, homozygotes for lethal genes—do not exist. Heterozygotes are detected only when they happen to be mated with each other and produce lethal offspring; they can then be discarded. When a male is to be used widely, especially for artificial insemination, planned crosses to detect the presence of lethal genes may be considered worthwhile. As shown in Fig. 19, the male is mated to a number of his daughters. About half of these will have inherited the lethal gene, and when these are backcrossed to their sire, there is a chance of 1 in 4 that a homozygous lethal calf will be produced. In the diagram this happens in the case of Fiona and Catriona, which have produced amputated calves. Lorna, Clarissa, and Moira, which likewise carry the lethal gene, have produced normal calves, but may produce amputated ones on repeated backcrossings to their sire. In any case, the occurrence of even one lethal calf in such a cross is sufficient to show that the bull carried the "amputated" gene.

There is no hard and fast distinction between lethal genes and other genes. All genes affect developmental processes and many mutant genes do so adversely. Whether or not these disturbances will be lethal depends on how essential the normal process is for the life of the organism. In a warm-blooded animal like a calf, a gene causing lack of hair is lethal; in the cold-blooded fly Drosophila, similar genes causing lack of bristles are not lethal. Moreover, one and the same gene may be lethal under one set of circumstances and harmless or moderately disabling under another. Blindness in wild dogs would almost certainly be lethal for pups; under domestication, even dogs born blind may reach old age. In man, a dominant gene produces malignant tumors of the retina which often result in early death. In a society without medical services, this gene would act as a near-lethal; in our modern society, affected children can be cured completely and permanently through

FIG. 19.

Progeny test of a bull for the presence of a recessive lethal (l). All the cows are daughters of the bull.

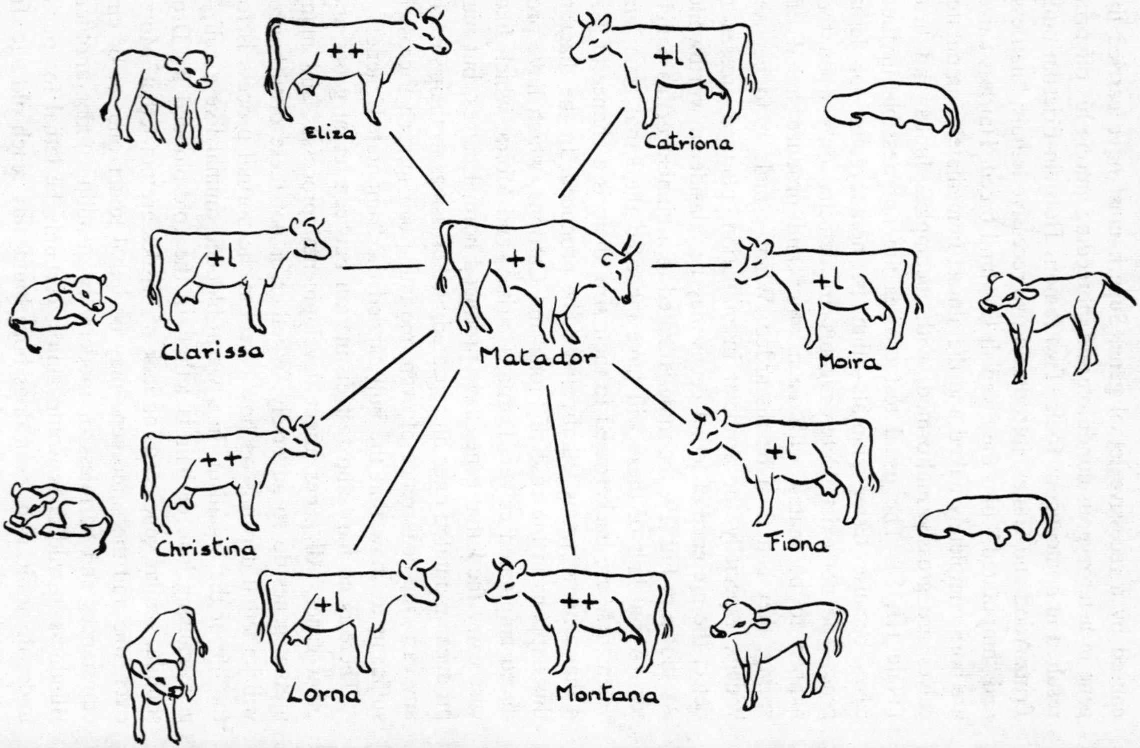

operation or irradiation, although they will be blind in one or both eyes. In Chapter 5 we saw that some strains of yeast have a gene which makes them unable to use galactose as a nutrient. On a galactose medium, this gene is lethal; on a glucose medium, it is harmless.

CHAPTER 9   *Of Monkeys and Men*

From the 23rd to the 30th of August, 1939, on the eve of the Second World War, geneticists from many countries met in Edinburgh for the Seventh International Congress of Genetics. While they debated in the southern part of the town, a practical experiment in genetics was carried out in the northern part, where three British geneticists confronted the chimpanzees of the Zoological Gardens. The animals, consisting of five males and three females, were offered drinks of sugar water to which a substance called phenylthiocarbamate (PTC for short) had been added. One male and one female seemed to enjoy the sweet drink; the others made grimaces of intense disgust, and one was so furious that he spat the whole mouthful at one of the watching professors. After the congress the three geneticists continued their experiment with chimpanzees in the two big Zoological Parks of London, Regent's Park and Whipsnade. Altogether, they tested 27 chimpanzees, 14 males and 13 females. Of these, 9 males and 11 females reacted with unmistakable signs of distaste and anger, while the remaining 7 drank the strange concoction with composure or pleasure. The latter group included one couple whose young daughter, Jaqueline, also was housed at Regent's Park. When Jaqueline was tested she showed the same unconcern as her parents. This pleased the geneticists; for it was just what they had predicted, and nothing pleases a scientist more than to find that one of his predictions has come true.

Let us now look at the background of this strange experiment.

In 1931 two chemists were working in a laboratory where PTC was being prepared. A few small crystals flew up into the air, and one of the chemists complained of the bitter taste of the dust. The other chemist found nothing wrong with the dust. When they tasted the crystals directly, the difference persisted: to the first chemist they appeared intensely bitter, the second one tasted absolutely nothing. This, of course, made the chemists curious to see which of them had an abnormal sense of taste. It turned out that both of them were normal in the sense that they reacted like a great many others; for when the crystals were given to men, women and children of different ages and races, each group contained some to whom they tasted bitter and others to whom they appeared entirely tasteless. A year later, at a meeting of the American Association for the Advancement of Science in New Orleans, this division of mankind into "tasters" and "nontasters" was demonstrated on a large scale; 2,550 visitors registered their reaction to PTC crystals in a voting machine; about two thirds of them were tasters, the rest nontasters.

Ability to taste PTC is thus neither normal nor abnormal. It has nothing to do with ordinary taste discrimination. It is not acquired by experience nor can it be learned by training. It is, as far as we can judge, an entirely irrelevant trait. For the geneticist, however, it has the great attraction that it is inherited as a simple Mendelian dominant, like round seed shape in peas or black coat color in dogs. Let us call the gene for tasting T, and its allele for nontasting t (we cannot use the sign $+$ in this case, because neither allele can be called the "normal" partner). Then all nontasters will be tt, and when two of them marry, all their children will be tt and nontasters like little Jaqueline, the daughter of two nontasting chimpanzees. Tasters may be either TT or Tt. In a marriage where either the father or the mother is TT, the children will be TT or Tt and will all be tasters; but when both parents are Tt, they may have a nontasting child, tt.

Why, you may ask, do geneticists squander so much interest on a human trait which is no more than a curiosity? The answer is simple: ability or inability to taste PTC is one of the few *normal* human characters which are governed by allelomorphs of a single gene and therefore segregate according to Mendel's first law. Most of the more obvious and important human variations, such as color of hair, eyes or skin, body size, facial features, etc., are due to the action and interaction of numerous genes. It is true that, by and large, brown eye color is dominant over blue, so that brown-eyed parents may have a blue-eyed child, while blue-eyed parents generally have only blue-eyed children. But there are many intermediate shades of eye color; these are brought about through the interplay of many different genes, and no simple rule of segregation can be applied to the way they are inherited. The same is true for red hair, which, in the main, is recessive to not red hair, for snub nose, which is recessive to Roman nose, and for a number of other normal variants of the human exterior. Finally, the so-called "graded" characters like stature or intelligence depend on so many genes as well as on environmental influences that any simple genetical analysis is ruled out.

Abnormal characters, on the other hand, quite often are due to the action of single genes. This is easily understood if we think of genes as controllers of developmental processes. Hundreds of genes have to interact harmoniously in order to produce, for example, a normally functioning eye. Some of these genes determine superficial traits, such as the color of the iris or the length of the lashes; mutations in them are easily integrated into normal development and give rise to the observed normal variation in color or shape of the eyes. But if a mutation occurs in one of the genes that govern the development of the actual apparatus for seeing—the optic nerve, the retina, the lens—the chances are high that the eye can no longer function properly. Individuals in whom such a mutated gene has disturbed development have impaired eyesight or are blind, and the transmission of the gene according to Mendel's first law can be followed through the incidence of similarly afflicted individuals in subsequent generations. The situation is comparable to what can be done to a complicated piece of machinery, say a motorcar: there is an almost unlimited possibility for superficial variations in color, shape, etc., but even minor changes in the engine may ruin its performance.

It is for this reason and not because only abnormalities are inherited that abnormalities and diseases provide the most frequent illustrations of Mendelian inheritance in man. In a way, this is fortunate; for, while prospective parents in general are indifferent to the color of the eyes or the shape of the nose of their future children, they often are worried about the possibility that their children may inherit an abnormal trait. It is about such hereditary disabilities that they or their physician may come to the geneticist for advice, and in cases of single-gene inheritance some predictions can usually be made. We shall see examples of this in Chapter 12. First, however, we shall consider one important group of normal human variants in which segregation follows Mendel's first law.

CHAPTER 10 *Human Blood Groups*

A PERSON who has had the measles once is extremely unlikely to get a second attack of the same disease; he is, as we say, immune to it. Many other infectious diseases confer immunity upon recovery, although not always for such a long period. Immunity is the result of a defense mechanism of the body against the invading microorganism. Antibodies are formed which combine with the microorganisms and often destroy them by, for example, clumping or dissolving them. Lasting immunity is found when the antibodies outlast the infection.

Antibodies are highly specific in their reactions. Measles are a virus, but a person who has acquired immunity against measles is not, for that reason, less likely to contract German measles or poliomyelitis or any other virus disease. The specificity of antibodies is a consequence of the manner in which they arise. When a microorganism gets inside a warm-blooded animal, its protein acts as an antigen, that is, it stimulates the production of antibodies by the infected individual. Proteins are highly complex molecules; they consist of thousands of atoms which are arranged into specific configurations. An antigen functions like a mold for shaping a host protein into its own mirror image (Fig. 20, 1, 2). When the antibody has become free of this mold it still "fits" the exact type of antigen by which it was produced, but no others (Fig. 20, 3, 4).

Not only the protein of microorganisms but any foreign protein

(1) The antigen (AG) meets a protein molecule of
the infected animal

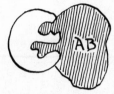

(2) The antibody (AB) is formed

(3) The antibody has become free of the antigen

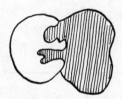 

(4) The antibody fits only the particular type of
antigen by which it was moulded

FIG. 20.
Antigen and antibody.

acts as antigen. This is the reason why no successful skin grafts can be made between different persons, not even between mother and child. No two individuals have exactly the same proteins in their skin cells, and when a graft is made it is eventually destroyed by the very antibodies whose formation it induces. In a later chapter we shall hear of one interesting exception to this rule.

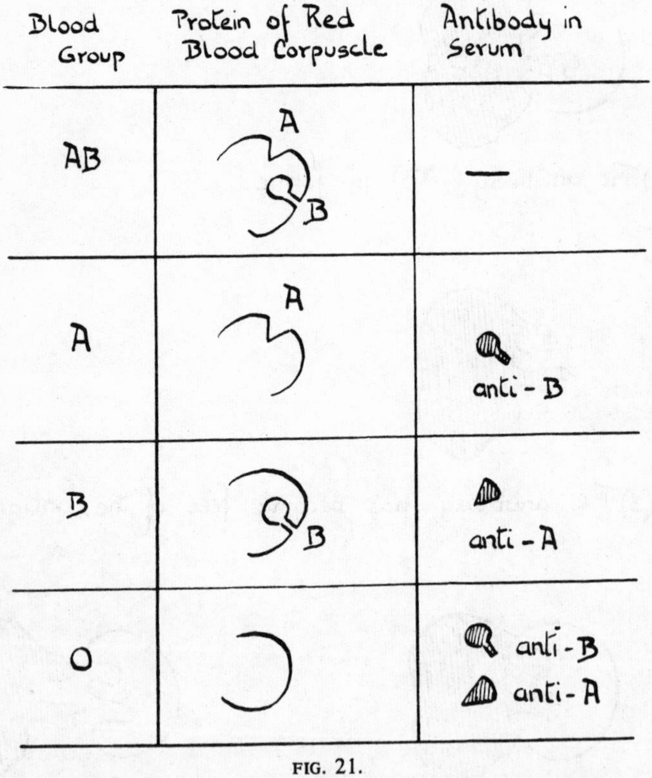

Blood Group	Protein of Red Blood Corpuscle	Antibody in Serum
AB	A / B (protein shapes)	—
A	A (protein shape)	anti-B
B	B (protein shape)	anti-A
O	(protein shape)	anti-B anti-A

FIG. 21.
Antigens and antibodies in the A-B-O human blood groups.

Antigens are also carried by the protein of the human blood cells. Fortunately, individual specificity is here less pronounced than in skin proteins; otherwise no transfusion of a patient with whole blood would be possible. Yet not every combination between donor and patient is compatible, and in the early days of blood transfusion fatal accidents arose from clots of transfused blood in the veins of a patient. The reason for this is now well understood, and such accidents are avoided by the right choice of donor.

A number of different antigens are carried by human red blood cells. Most of them can be detected only by the fact that they induce antibodies when the blood is injected into a warm-blooded animal, for example, a rabbit. But there is one group of antigens for which ready-made antibodies occur in human serum, the fluid in which the blood cells are suspended. The main antigens of this group are called A and B, and human beings can be divided into four groups according to whether their red blood cells carry one of these antigens (A or B), both (AB), or neither (O). In addition, the serum of each individual contains preformed antibodies to those antigens that are not present in the blood cells (Fig. 21). Thus, in blood group A the serum contains anti-B, in blood group B it contains anti-A, in blood group O it contains anti-A and anti-B, and in blood group AB it contains neither. For successful transfusion the donor has to be chosen so that his blood is not clotted by the antibodies of the patient.

It is probable that all antigenic specificities are gene controlled. In many cases this has been shown to be true. The A-B-O blood groups are determined by the action of three alleles of one gene; if, for the sake of simplicity, we waive the rule that alleles of the same gene should be denoted by the same letter, we may call these alleles A, B, and O. Let us pause for a moment to consider in which way this case differs from previously considered ones. In all previous examples we were dealing with *pairs* of alleles: round and wrinkled, red and white, tasting and nontasting. There is, however, no reason why any given gene should exist in only two alternative forms. Indeed we know of many cases of so-called "multiple alleles" in which a gene has mutated to a series of different alleles. One of these is illustrated in Fig. 22. It shows a wild rabbit and three mutant varieties, produced by the action of multiple alleles of a gene controlling coat color. The chinchilla rabbit has silvery fur; the Himalayan rabbit is white apart from black ears, feet, nose and tip of tail, and it has pink eyes; the albino rabbit is wholly white with pink eyes. The alleles producing these effects are usually denoted by the letters C for full (wild) color; c^{ch} for chinchilla; c^H for Himalayan; and c for albino. Any individual can, of course, carry only two of these genes and can be either homozygous for one of them, like the rabbits in the diagram, or heterozygous for two, for example, $c^H c$. In heterozygotes, coat color depends on the dominance relationship between the two alleles; since c^H is dominant over c, $c^H c$ rabbits look Himalayan.

Wild Type

Chinchilla

cc

$c^{ch} c^{ch}$

Himalayan

Albino

$c^H c^H$

cc

FIG. 22.
Multiple alleles in the rabbit.

The possible genotypes for A, B, and O in man and the blood groups that correspond to them are set out in the following table:

	homozygous			heterozygous		
Genotype	OO	AA	BB	AO	BO	AB
Blood group	O	A	B	A	B	AB

You will notice that each gene produces its characteristic antigen independent of its partner gene. As a result O, which does not produce an antigen, cannot be recognized in the presence of either A or B. In other words, O is recessive to A and B, and persons of blood group A or B can be of two different genotypes according to whether or not they are heterozygous for O. This, as we shall see presently, plays an important role in the medicolegal application of the A-B-O blood groups.

Newborn infants in maternity wards are labeled with the name of the mother. Very occasionally doubt may arise as to whether a mother has been given the right baby, and blood typing may then help to decide this question. In a well-known case a woman, let us call her Mrs. Smith, found on her return from the hospital that her baby carried the label "Brown." There had been a Mrs. Brown in the same ward as Mrs. Smith, and she had, indeed, been given an infant labeled "Smith." The question arose: What had been exchanged, the labels or the babies? Blood typing showed that Mr. and Mrs. Brown belonged to blood group O. A glance at the table

FIG. 23.

A paternity problem that cannot be decided from the evidence of the A-B-O blood groups.

will show you that between them they carried nothing but O genes and could not have a child with any blood group but O. On the other hand, the Smiths could *not* have a child of blood group O; for, while Mrs. Smith belonged to blood group O, Mr. Smith belonged to AB. He was, therefore heterozygous for A and B, and had to transmit one of these alleles to his child. When it was found that baby "Brown" was O and Baby "Smith" was A, it was evident that the labels were correct and that the two women had been given the wrong infants.

Not all cases can be decided so easily and unambiguously. Suppose that both Smith and Brown parents had belonged to blood group A. Then either couple might have produced baby "Smith" with blood group A. Moreover, either couple might have produced baby "Brown" with blood group O; for A individuals may carry O genes and can transmit them to their children. Fortunately, many more blood groups, controlled by different series of alleles, have been discovered in recent years and can be used for deciding difficult cases.

This refers also to the use of blood-typing in cases of disputed paternity, many of which cannot be decided on the basis of the A-B-O system alone. Mr. Smith, as we just saw, could not have fathered a child of blood group O; similarly, Mr. and Mrs. Brown could not have produced a child belonging to blood group A, B, or AB. But the father of an A baby from an A mother might belong to any of the four major blood groups, as can readily be seen from the table and from Fig. 23. In such a dilemma, recourse to other blood groups may help narrow the issue. In any case, blood-group tests in cases of disputed paternity fulfill only a negative function; they can exclude certain men from possible fatherhood, but they cannot indict any particular man. Suppose our Mr. Brown of blood group O were alleged to be the father of an illegitimate child of blood group O by a woman of blood group B. On purely genetical grounds, there is no objection to this assumption, but neither is there an objection to any other man of blood group O or against any men of blood groups A and B. Only where the baby shares a very rare blood group with the alleged father, but not with the mother, will the geneticist feel reasonably convinced of the correctness of the allegation, although the court may not accept his judgment. In 1921 a Norwegian judge made medicolegal history by convicting a man of paternity on account of a rare dominant abnormality—foreshortened fingers, or "brachydactyly"—which was absent in the mother but present in both the infant and the alleged father.

CHAPTER 11   *Danger to Infants*

LIKE THE ALLELES which determine ability or inability to taste PTC, the A, B and O blood-group alleles occur not only in human beings but also in the large anthropoid apes. A new and highly important human blood group was discovered in 1940 through tests on lower monkeys. When rabbits were injected with blood from a Rhesus monkey, their serum was found to contain an antibody which combined with the red blood cells of about 85 per cent of individuals in a White population; the remaining 15 per cent gave no such reaction. Persons whose blood reacts with the antibody against Rhesus blood are called Rh-positive; those who do not react are called Rh-negative. Both types of individual occur in all human races, but the proportions of positives and negatives differ. Evidently the red blood cells of Rh-positive individuals carry an antigen which is so similar to the antigen on the Rhesus blood cells that the antibody does not distinguish between them. The blood cells of Rh-negative persons lacks this antigen (Fig. 24).

When an Rh-negative person is given a blood transfusion from an Rh-positive donor, his body reacts like that of a rabbit into which Rhesus antigen is injected: it makes antibodies against the foreign antigen. Since it takes some time before a sufficient amount of antibody is produced, a first transfusion of this kind is usually perfectly harmless; but the antibodies persist in the serum of the transfused person, and should he receive a second transfusion with Rh-positive blood there may be a severe reaction. This explains why accidents had happened occasionally in blood transfusions

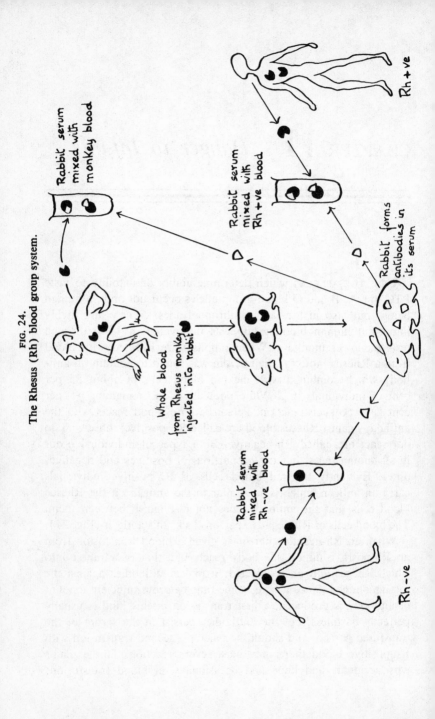

FIG. 24.
The Rhesus (Rh) blood group system.

Rabbit serum mixed with monkey blood

Rabbit serum mixed with Rh +ve blood

Rabbit serum mixed with Rh -ve blood

Whole blood from Rhesus monkey injected into rabbit

Rabbit forms antibodies in its serum

Rh +ve

Rh -ve

between individuals of the same A-B-O blood group. No antibodies are formed by an Rh-positive individual who is given a transfusion with Rh-positive blood: for such a patient the Rh-antigen is not a foreign antigen.

Of much greater importance is the fact that the new blood group furnished the explanation for a severe and hitherto rather mysterious disease, called "hemolytic disease of the newborn." Before we go into this, we shall have to consider the inheritance of the Rh character. At first sight it is very simple. Rh-positive children invariably have at least one Rh-positive parent. Rh-negative children, on the other hand, may issue from any combination of parents: both Rh-positive, or one Rh-positive, the other Rh-negative. Thus Rh-positive parents may carry the Rh-negative gene and transmit it to their children, while Rh-negative parents carry only Rh-negative genes. Expressed in Mendelian terms, this means that we are dealing with a dominant allele, *Rh,* and a recessive allele, *rh*. Rh-negative individuals must be homozygous (*rh rh*), but Rh-positive individuals may be homozygous (*Rh Rh*) or heterozygous (*Rh rh*). In reality, more alleles are known and the situation is far from simple; but for most practical purposes these complications can be disregarded.

With this simple genetical picture in mind, let us return to hemolytic disease of the newborn. About once in several hundred pregnancies among White women, a newborn child suffers from a severe anemia with jaundice which in the worst cases may be fatal if blood transfusion cannot be carried out in time. The disease has a tendency to affect several children in the same family, and this seemed to point to a hereditary basis; but there are also special features which do not fit into any simple Mendelian explanation. Thus first-born children hardly ever are affected; but once a couple have had one hemolytic child, more of their children are likely to be affected. In some families all children following the birth of the first affected one suffer from the disease. The explanation came when it was found that in almost all cases of hemolytic disease the mother was Rh-negative and the child Rh-positive and that, moreover, the blood of the mother contained anti-Rh antibody. On the contrary, no such antibody is found in the blood of Rh-negative women who never have been pregnant or who have given birth only to Rh-negative children. This shows that an Rh-negative woman reacts to an Rh-positive fetus as she would to transfusion with Rh-positive blood: she makes antibodies against the Rh-antigen (Fig. 25, 1). As after blood transfusion, the level of antibodies takes time to build up and usually no reaction occurs with the fetus that stimulated antibody production. This explains why first-born chil-

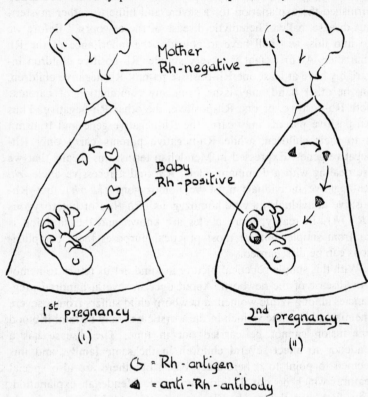

Mother
Rh-negative ——

Baby
Rh-positive

1st pregnancy
(I)

2nd pregnancy
(II)

G = Rh - antigen
= anti-Rh-antibody

FIG. 25.
Antibodies in an Rh-negative mother carrying
an Rh-positive fetus.

dren rarely suffer from hemolytic disease. But when an Rh-negative woman is pregnant with a second Rh-positive child her antibodies may get into the circulation of the fetus and destroy its blood cells (Fig. 25, 2).

When an Rh-negative woman bears an Rh-positive child, the *Rh* gene in the fetus must have come from the father's side. The father,

r-negative mare has given birth to an R-positive foal

r-negative mare suckles foal herself

R-positive foal fostered out to R-positive mare

Foal dies

Foal thrives

FIG. 26.
An Rh-like blood group system in horses. The antibodies do not affect the embryo, but are present in the mare's milk.

therefore is either homozygous, *Rh Rh,* or heterozygous, *Rh rh.* In the former case, he will transit an *Rh* gene to every child; this is the type of marriage where, once a sufficiently high level of antibodies has been established in the mother, every child will be affected. In the second case, half the children will inherit an *rh* gene from both father and mother and will be Rh-negative; these children are in no danger from the antibodies in the mother's blood. Fortunately, a large proportion of pregnancies which, from the blood groups of father and mother, might lead to hemolytic disease of the newborn do not, in fact, do so, partly because of the low level of antibodies in early pregnancies, partly because of differences in the ease with which antigens and antibodies are exchanged between mother and child, partly perhaps for still other reasons. All the same, many hospitals make sure that pregnancies of an Rh-negative mother and an Rh-positive father get special attention. In severe cases, an affected child may be saved by the replacement of all its blood with blood that is free from antibodies.

Similar gene-controlled incompatibilities between the blood groups of mother and offspring are known in a number of animal species, for example, rabbits, dogs, and horses. Not always, however, do the antibodies harm the fetus before birth. In the horses, for example, antibodies are produced when a stallion, carrying on its blood cells an antigen *R* sires a foal with this antigen by a mare lacking it (labelled *r*—in Fig. 26). The mare produces antibodies against *R,* but it takes at least three pregnancies by an *R* stallion before the danger limit has been reached. In a subsequent pregnancy by an *R* stallion, the antibodies in the mother's milk may kill the foal; but the foal may be saved by fostering it out to another mare.

CHAPTER 12   *Genetics Counseling*

As the knowledge that many diseases and abnormalities have a hereditary basis becomes more widespread, potential parents are more often worried about their biological responsibility toward their offspring. Directly, or through their physician, they may ask genetical advice on whether they should marry a relative, or should marry at all, or—if already married—should have children. The answer is rarely simple. Human genetics is still a very young science, hardly two human generations old. Only a few abnormalities and diseases have been clearly recognized as being due to a dominant or a recessive gene. For these, the geneticist can often predict the risk involved in producing a child. Sometimes he can state with certainty that the risk is negligible; he can rarely, on the contrary, warn the prospective parents that their child will almost certainly be abnormal. Usually he can only estimate the probability of such an event. He may, for example, tell parents who already had one deaf child that their next child has a chance of 1 in 4 of being likewise deaf. Whether or not the parents are going to take this risk depends on their own decision.

Many complicating factors have to be considered in genetic counseling. Modern clinical means of diagnosing an abnormal condition are highly refined compared with what they were a hundred years ago; but compared with the developmental events which precede a recognizable abnormality they are crude. Cataract in a newborn child may be caused by the action of a gene; it may also be due to a virus that, early in pregnancy, produced an attack of

German measles in the mother and a profound disturbance of lens development in the embryo. Clinically, the two types of cataract look the same; but, while the first type is hereditary, the second is not. In such a case the genetic counselor will not only need to know the incidence of cataract in the families of both parents, he will also need information on the illnesses of the mother during pregnancy. There are many similar cases in which external influences, whose nature often is unknown, produce effects that are indistinguishable from those of harmful mutant genes. Cleft palate and harelip often are hereditary, but they may also occur as nonhereditary results of developmental accidents. A prospective mother may be deaf through gene action or she may be deaf as a result of scarlet fever in infancy. In all such cases, the geneticist will have to decide whether, in any particular instance, he is dealing with a genetical defect, which may reappear in the children, or with an acquired abnormality, which will not do so. Family histories are his main standby. When he finds that several members of the family suffer from the same abnormality he will be inclined to attribute this to the action of a gene, especially when it is already known that the abnormality—say, cleft palate—often is hereditary. But the converse is not always true: an abnormality may be hereditary even when it appears in only one member of a family. This is obvious for the effects of recessive genes; for these genes are carried hidden in heterozygotes, and even in a fairly extensive pedigree affected individuals may be lacking simply because by chance the recorded individuals do not include homozygotes. Rarely it may happen that a dominant abnormality arises through mutation in a family that hitherto had been entirely free of the defect.

These are not all the difficulties that confront the genetical counselor. He has also to keep in mind that many harmful genes are not fully "penetrant," that is, that persons who, by virtue of their genes, would be expected to be abnormal or diseased are, in fact, normal and healthy. In Chapter 8 we saw that this is true even for lethal genes, which in certain circumstances may be more or less harmless. Many harmful genes in man show their effects only in a proportion of individuals. Diabetes has a genetical basis; but in addition to diabetics who are cured by insulin there are others who have the genotype for diabetes but never develop the disease. Similarly, not every child that inherited the gene for retinoblastoma (tumor of the retina, see below) develops tumors. The conditions which produce these fortunate exceptions are unknown; when we know more about them we may be able to use preventive measures against hereditary abnormalities and diseases. The genetical adviser, however, has to keep in mind that individuals in whom a harmful gene fails to manifest itself are, for this reason, not less likely than visibly affected persons to transmit the gene to their children, where it may become manifest.

A final complication which plays an important role in genetic counseling is the fact that different genes, possibly by different primary disturbances of development, may produce the same final result. Thus retinitis pigmentosa, a progressive deterioration of the retina leading to blindness, may be due to at least two different genes, one dominant and the other recessive. In any particular case, the genetical prognosis depends on which gene is responsible; family histories are necessary to decide this question.

These general considerations will be best understood if we illustrate them by a few examples of genetical counseling:

EXAMPLE 1: RETINOBLASTOMA.

The dominant gene causing this exceedingly severe condition has already been mentioned. A condition which is clinically indistinguishable from hereditary retinoblastoma may arise from unknown developmental disturbances; this is not transmissible to the progeny.

The Problem.

Two brothers, John and Edward, consult the geneticist about the advisability of having children. Their mother was operated on for retinoblastoma at the age of 2 and, in consequence of the operation, is blind in one eye. Their father and two younger brothers have normal eyesight. So has Edward; but John and a young sister had to be operated upon as children and are totally blind. Both brothers are married to normal-sighted women.

The Advice.

The occurrence of retinoblastoma in the mother and two children shows that John suffers from the hereditary form of the disease.

Like his mother, he is heterozygous for the gene *Rb,* having received the normal allelomorph + from his father. His genotype, therefore, is *Rb* +. Since half his spermatozoa carry the *Rb* gene, every child of his has a 50 per cent chance of being born with this terrible disability. It is true that occasionally a child with the *Rb* gene may escape its effect; but this consideration tips the balance only slightly in favor of normal-sighted children. This is one of the cases in which the geneticist will feel justified in issuing a grave warning against procreation.

Edward's case is very different. If the geneticist could be sure that the *Rb* gene invariably results in observable disease, he would be able to reassure Edward completely; for in this case Edward obviously would be among the fortunate fifty per cent of his mother's children to whom she transmitted the normal allele of *Rb*. Since, however, the gene is not fully penetrant, there is a slight possibility that Edward, like John, may be genotypically *Rb* + and, like John, will transmit the gene to half his children. All the same, the risk is not great; the geneticist, having explained the situation to Edward, will leave it to him and his wife to make the final decision.

EXAMPLE 2: HUNTINGTON'S CHOREA.

This is a rare and terrible disorder of the nervous system, caused by a dominant gene with 100 per cent penetrance. In one particular family, over 1,000 cases have been recorded in 300 years. Almost invariably, an affected person has an affected father or mother. In the few exceptional cases, one of the parents died young and, presumably, carried the gene *Hc,* which hardly ever shows its effect in young persons. In many people's minds there is a confusion between hereditary and congenital diseases. The former are due to the action of genes; the latter are present at birth. These two features have little to do with one another. We saw already that congenital abnormalities, e.g., cataract and harelip, need not be caused by genes; conversely, hereditary diseases may affect the patient long after birth. Thus persons carrying the *Hc* gene may yet escape its effect if they happen to die young. Those, however, who live to late middle age invariably develop the symptoms, which consist of violent and uncontrollable jerkings and twitchings, usually accompanied by mental and emotional deterioration.

The Problem.

A child placement agency wants to find homes for three children: Joan, aged 6; Mary, aged 5; Stephen, aged 2. All three children are related and come from a family several members of which have suffered from Huntington's chorea. The agency wishes to know whether the foster parents of any or all of these children run the risk of having to care for a seriously disabled child.

The Advice.

First of all, there is little danger that any of the children—whether or not they carry the harmful gene *Hc*—will develop chorea while still under the care of their foster parents; for the first symptoms rarely appear before the age of 25, and often they appear much later. Prospective foster parents who are mainly interested in the more immediate future may therefore safely adopt any of these children. They may, however, wish to avoid the risk of seeing a person of whom they have grown fond develop the disease later in life. This risk can be estimated from the family history of the children.

Figure 27 shows a pedigree of the family through three generations backward. It is a typical pedigree of a dominant disease. Every affected person has one affected parent (father or mother), and the disease is carried through the generations in a chain of affected individuals. Genotypically, all affected persons have inherited the *Hc* gene from their affected parent and the normal allele from the healthy parent; they are therefore heterozygotes, *Hc* +. While all affected persons carry the *Hc* gene, the converse is not true; for among the healthy persons there may be some who, because of the late onset of the disease, carry the gene and may transmit it to their progeny. Without this complication there would, in fact, not be any necessity for consulting a geneticist about the presence or absence of the *Hc* gene. Since age plays such an important role in the manifestation of the gene, the ages of all relevant individuals are given in the legend to Fig. 27.

The geneticist's conclusions are as follows:

Mary is the gravest risk. Since her father suffers from chorea, his genotype is *Hc* +, and Mary has a 50 per cent chance of having inherited the *Hc* gene.

For *Stephen* the forecast is somewhat more hopeful, although still serious. His grandmother, Laura, who is also Mary's grandmother, was a heterozygote; thus there is a 50 per cent chance that Stephen's mother, Anna, may have inherited the *Hc* gene from Laura. It is true that Anna so far shows no symptoms of chorea;

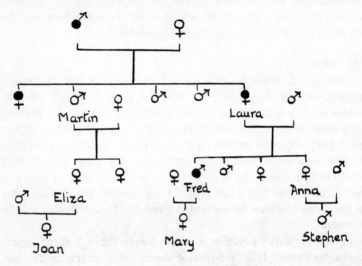

[Ages of relevant individuals:

Martin (at death) — 69 yrs.
Laura   ("   ")   — 60 yrs.
Eliza (living)   — 30 yrs.
Fred (")   — 39 yrs.
Anna (")   — 28 yrs.
Joan   — 6 yrs.
Mary   — 5 yrs.
Stephen   — 2 yrs.]

FIG. 27.
Pedigree of Huntington's chorea.

but as she is only 28 years of age, this does not mean that she is free from the gene. If she is, then Stephen, too, will be genotypically sound; if Anna is heterozygous, then Stephen—like Mary—has a 50 per cent chance of carrying the *Hc* gene. Altogether, Stephen's chance of being a heterozygote are 50 per cent of 50 per cent, that is, one half of one half, or one quarter. If Stephen is an otherwise healthy and well-developed child, the foster parents may be prepared to take this risk.

Joan is the only one of the three children for whom the genetical outlook is wholly good. It is true that her mother, Eliza, is still of an age at which the disease usually remains hidden; but, since Eliza's father, Martin, died healthy at an advanced age, he almost certainly was free of the gene, and the disease has disappeared from his branch of the family.

EXAMPLE 3: AMAUROTIC IDIOCY.

This sad and fatal condition of infants is due to a defect in the chemistry of the brain cells, resulting in blindness, mental degeneration, and early death. It is caused by a rare recessive gene. A similar abnormality, affecting older children, is due to the action of a different gene.

The Problem.

A healthy and intelligent young couple, George and Marion, have had an amaurotic baby. They want to know whether there is a possibility that any further children of theirs will be similarly affected. At the same time, George wants advice about two projected marriages in his family: his brother Bernard wishes to marry Marion's sister Esther and his younger brother William, who is studying abroad, is engaged to be married to a co-student. George wants to spare his brothers the distress he has just suffered through the birth of an abnormal child. He has brought a pedigree of his closest family (Fig. 28).

The Advice.

The pedigree is in agreement with the established fact that amaurotic idiocy is caused by a recessive gene. Unlike a dominant gene, a recessive gene may remain hidden for many generations in heterozygotes, until a marriage between two heterozygotes provides the chance for a homozygous child to be born. If we call the gene for amaurotic idiocy *a,* the affected child must be homozygous, *aa.* Since it must have inherited one of the two *a* genes from each of its parents, both Marion and George are heterozygotes $(a+)$. When a gene is as rare as the one we are dealing with, the chance that two heterozygotes marry is generally very small; but in the present case it is increased by the fact that George and Marion are first cousins and evidently have inherited the *a* gene from one of their common grandparents. Thus not only George and Marion, but also their mothers and either their grandfather or grandmother must have been heterozygous for *a*. How long the gene had been carried in this family cannot be decided from the scanty family records.

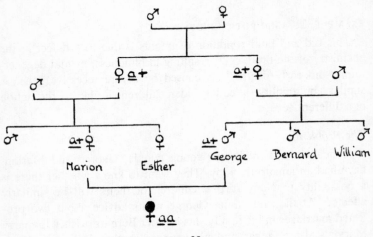

FIG. 28.
Pedigree of amaurotic idiocy.

First question.

Since both Marion and George are heterozygotes (*a*+), the chance that any child of theirs receives the harmful gene through both ovum and spermatozoon is ½ of ½, that is, ¼. Thus the odds against the next or any further child being similarly afflicted as the first-born are 3:1. In view of the distressing nature of the disease, this is a serious risk to take.

Second question.

Bernard and Esther have the same parents as Marion. Marion's mother, as we saw, was heterozygous for *a*; half of her ova must have carried the gene, and thus each of her children had a chance of ½ of receiving it. Marion was among the unlucky 50 per cent; whether or not this is true also for Esther, it is not possible to say. The same applies to Bernard, who, like Esther, has a 50 per cent chance of being a heterozygote for *a*. At worst, both Esther and Bernard are *a*+; then their children, like those of Marion and George, run a 25 per cent risk of being born abnormal. At best, both Esther and Bernard have inherited the normal allele from their mother and are ++; then their offspring is in no danger from the *a* gene. In between are two possibilities: Esther may be ++ and Bernard *a*+, or Bernard may be ++ and Esther *a*+. In either case, all children will be healthy because none of them can inherit the harmful gene from both parents; but half the children will carry the gene and will themselves have to consider the risk of producing an idiotic child. On the whole, it can be calculated that the chance of Esther and Bernard having a defective child is 1 in 16; as the disease is so severe, they may well consider this risk too high.

Third question.

William, like his brothers, has a chance of 50 per cent of being heterozygous for *a;* but, since the frequency of the *a* gene in the general population is low, there is little danger that his fiancée, too, will be heterozygous. Thus there is no reason for advising William against his projected marriage or against having children; but he should be advised to inform his children of the possible presence of this harmful gene in their genotype, and to warn them against marrying a relative from the father's side.

CHAPTER 13 *Eugenics*

THE TERM "EUGENICS" was invented by Francis Galton, a younger cousin of Charles Darwin. Literally, eugenics means the study of being "wellborn"; for Galton, this meant being born with a genetical endowment for physical and mental excellence. He was the first to realize that modern man, himself a product of millions of years of natural evolution, was rapidly accumulating knowledge and techniques that should enable him to take a hand in influencing the further evolution of his own species in a similar way as he has already influenced the evolution of domestic animals and plants.

Eugenics cannot be discussed on a purely biological level; it involves value judgments that cannot be separated from the biological problem without making nonsense of the whole concept. This will become clear if we compare three types of selection: (1) natural selection, which is the guiding force in evolution; (2) the artificial selection of domestic animals and plants; (3) the kind of selection that is envisaged by the advocates of eugenics.

(1) We shall deal with natural selection and evolution more fully in Chapter 29. At the moment it is sufficient to state the simple principle of natural selection, as it was first recognized by Charles Darwin and A. R. Wallace. It takes account of the evident fact that individuals best fitted to survive and reproduce under the conditions of their environment will leave more progeny than the less fitted ones; it follows that those genes that made some parents have more progeny than the rest will become more frequent

among the progeny than they were among the generation of the parents. Let us illustrate this by an example. Suppose that in a certain region the climate becomes very cold. Then rabbits with thick fur will survive and reproduce better than rabbits with sparse fur, and in the next generation a larger proportion of baby rabbits will come from thick-furred than from thin-furred parents. Now, differences in thickness of fur may have all kinds of causes: nutrition, disease, the climate itself. But to some extent gene differences certainly are involved, and it is safe to assume that many of the thick-furred parent rabbits had a thick fur because of a certain type of genes. At least some of these genes will be transmitted to the young, and since the progeny of the thick-furred rabbits is more numerous than that of the thin-furred ones, the proportion of animals with genes for thick fur will be greater among the children than among the parental generation. If the climate persists cold, this process will go on through the generations, until eventually a breed of rabbits may be formed in which all individuals have genes for thick fur.

Natural selection knows only one criterion of fitness: the ability to survive and leave live offspring. Whether individuals that are fittest by this criterion are also superior in other respects—whether, for instance, they are prettier, or cleverer, or braver—does not enter the picture, except, of course, where beauty or cleverness or courage makes an individual more likely to leave more progeny. If, among our rabbits, the ugliest, stupidest, and most cowardly ones should happen to be better adapted to a cold climate, then natural selection would produce an ugly, stupid, and more than usually timid breed of rabbits with superbly thick fur.

(2) Similarly, when man wants to improve his domesticated plants and animals he tries to obtain as many offspring as possible from certain selected individuals, and he destroys others before they can reproduce. But, although both natural and artificial selection use the same means, their ends are quite different. In natural selection, ends and means are one and the same: the greatest possible number of live progeny. Artificial selection acts toward ends that are dictated by human value judgments. Man wants cereals that produce a heavy yield of nourishing grains. He wants fowl that lay many and large eggs. He wants dogs that can be trained to hunt for their master instead of for themselves. Often

the aims of artificial selection run counter to the demands of natural selection. Few of our domesticated animals or plants would be able to survive if left to themselves. Every gardener knows to his grief that his vegetables and flowers are lamentably inferior to weeds in the one point that counts in natural selection: the ability to multiply.

(3) Eugenics wants to apply the method of artificial selection to mankind by encouraging individuals with desirable genes to produce offspring, and discouraging individuals with undesirable genes from doing so. This program requires answers to two questions: (1) What are desirable and what are undesirable traits in man? (2) To what extent and in which way are these traits inherited? The second question refers to facts that, in principle, can be established by the application of modern genetical knowledge to observations on human families. It is true that at present we know much more about the genetics of fruit flies, cattle, or corn than about that of our own species; but this is sure to change in the course of the next generations. The first question refers to value judgments and cannot, therefore, be answered in an objective and unanimously accepted way. It is, however, fairly easy to reach agreement about what constitutes decidedly undesirable traits such as blindness, deafness, imbecility, and insanity. Moreover, for reasons explained before (p. 60), the genetics of abnormal human traits is much better known and, often, much simpler than that of normal traits. Therefore, eugenical measures so far are mainly limited to attempts at preventing the transmission of decidedly undesirable genes to future generations. This part of the eugenics program is often called "negative eugenics." Genetics counseling of the type discussed in the previous chapter is one of the methods of negative eugenics. A more drastic method consists of sterilizing carriers of highly undesirable genes.

NEGATIVE EUGENICS

Laws for sterilizing on eugenical grounds exist in many European and American states. They are usually on a voluntary basis and require the consent of the affected person or of his or her guardian. The oldest law of this kind was passed in Sweden in 1757. It banned marriage of epileptics, and it took account of the observation that only a certain type of epilepsy (now called "endogenous") is hereditary and, therefore, fell within the scope of the law. Nowadays sterilization is effected by a minor operation whose only result is to prevent the passage of spermatozoa or ova.

In states with sterilization laws, some of the persons whose cases we discussed in Chapter 12 might well have made successful application to be sterilized for their own protection. The main purpose of eugenic sterilization, however, is not the prevention of private tragedies but the elimination of highly undesirable genes from the human race. We may ask ourselves how far this aim is likely to be achieved. First of all, it should be said that complete elimination of a harmful gene is not possible. For, if a gene has once arisen through mutation, it will do so again, and even if we should be able to get rid of all existing genes for, say, Huntington's chorea, new ones will be produced by mutation. However, mutation is such a rare event (see Chap. 27) that the frequency of most harmful genes could be kept low indeed if we eliminated all existing ones. How well this can be done depends on the type of gene. A dominant gene with complete penetrance shows up in every person carrying it; if all these persons were sterilized, the existing genes would be eliminated within one generation, and when new genes of the same kind arose by mutation they could be eliminated equally readily. Such genes, however, are very rare. Retinoblastoma is one of the few cases in question. Huntington's chorea, too, is due to a highly undesirable dominant gene with complete penetrance; but the effects of the gene often appear too late to prevent the production of progeny. All the same, sterilization of individuals suffering from certain severe dominant disabilities is bound to reduce the frequency of the responsible genes in future generations. The frequency of the most harmful dominant genes will, however, be hardly affected by sterilization; for these genes, by killing or sterilizing their carriers, are self-eliminating, and most new occurrences of such diseases are not due to inheritance but to mutation.

The situation is entirely different for recessive abnormalities. Here sterilization may still be desirable from the point of view of the individual family, as when parents of one amaurotic child wish to avoid having a second one like it; from the point of view of the human population, sterilization against recessive abnormalities is exceedingly ineffective. This is due to the fact that recessive genes, by their very nature, may be carried hidden in outwardly normal individuals. Sterilization of the visibly affected homozygotes leaves the heterozygotes free to transmit the harmful gene. Now it can be shown that harmful recessive genes occur more frequently in heterozygotes than in homozygotes, the more so the rarer they are. An easy way of visualizing this is the following: Imagine a town in which 10 per cent of all men and women carry a harmful recessive gene r. Since the presence of the gene in heterozygotes cannot be detected, it cannot influence the choice of marriage partners. Thus when a man who himself carries the gene r together with its normal allele chooses a wife he is 9 times as liable to choose one who is free of the gene as one who likewise is heterozygous for it (Fig. 29, above). Whoever he marries, he will transmit the gene to some of his children, who therefore will be heterozygotes like their father; but only 1 out of 9 possible marriages that he may make can give rise to homozygous children who will exhibit the bad effects of the gene. Now consider a second, rarer, gene s for which only 1 in 1,000 persons is heterozygous. When a heterozygote for s chooses a wife (Fig. 29, below) the chance that he will choose another heterozygote is only 1 in 1,000, and while all 1,000 possible marriages can give rise to heterozygotes, only 1 can give rise to homozygotes. It is easy to make more precise estimates of the relative frequencies of heterozygotes and homozygotes for recessive genes. When, for example, 1 in 100 individuals is homozygous for such a gene, 18 times as many will be heterozygous for it; when only 1 in 10,000 is homozygous, there will be almost 200 times as many heterozygotes.

Now, highly undesirable recessive genes are rare in human populations. This is so in spite of the obvious fact that a great many individuals suffer from severe abnormalities such as blindness or feeble-mindedness; for only a fraction of these abnormalities are due to gene action and, moreover, the same type of abnormality may be due to a number of different genes, so that each gene by itself is rare. If we, then, take together the two facts that (1) most recessive harmful genes are rare and (2) rare recessive genes are carried much more often in heterozygotes than in homozygotes, we can easily see that the prospects for getting rid of these genes by sterilizing the rare homozygotes are poor. It would take thousands of years to effect a noticeable reduction of recessive diseases by continued sterilization of the homozygotes. One exceptional type of recessive gene to which this statement does not apply will be discussed in Chapter 15.

The preceding calculations have been made on the assumption that marriage partners are not blood relatives. Marriage between

FIG. 29.

Choice of a wife by a man carrying a harmful recessive gene. Above: 1 out of 10 women is heterozygous for the same gene. Below: 1 out of 1,000 women is heterozygous.

relatives greatly increases the chance that both may be heterozygous for the same harmful recessive gene and may produce abnormal children. We have seen an example of this in the case of George and Marion, discussed in the previous chapter. Theirs is not an exceptional case; it has indeed been found that frequently the parents of amaurotic babies are related to each other. A search through medical literature showed that among about 130 European cases of this disease, at least 15 per cent of the parents were first cousins, while another 12–16 per cent were related to a less close degree. This has to be compared with the fact that in the general European population less than 1 per cent of all marriages are between first cousins. An unusually high incidence of cousin marriages has also been found among the parents of children suffering from other rare recessive abnormalities. In fact, geneticists have reversed the argument: if they find that a certain abnormality or disease tends to occur among the children of related parents, they take this as an indication that it may be due to a recessive gene.

If, as in Roman Catholic communities, cousin marriages were forbidden in the whole population, the incidence of recessive abnormalities like amaurotic idiocy, deaf-mutism, and albinism would be cut down considerably. This eugenical benefit would, however, be derived entirely from a minority of families in which a harmful recessive gene happened to be transmitted, and it would be gained at the expense of the majority of potential marriages which would have resulted in normal children. A complete ban on cousin marriage is, therefore, hardly justifiable on these grounds except, perhaps, with a view to reducing the risk of stillbirths or early deaths of infants; for these occur considerably more often in cousin marriages than in the general population, presumably because cousins more often are heterozygous for the same recessive lethal gene. In any case, it is important that persons who contemplate marrying a relative should be made aware of the possible dangers of such a step. They should be advised to gather as much information about their family as possible and to consult a geneticist when they find that the same abnormality has occurred repeatedly among their relatives, even among quite distant ones.

It is evident that marriages between relatives will be more frequent in small isolated communities than in large populous places. If such a community happens to carry a harmful recessive gene which arose by mutation or was introduced by an immigrant, inbreeding will result in an unusually high incidence of abnormal children. Indeed, while many small communities have no more physically or mentally handicapped members than the population at large, there are some in which a certain defect, say blindness or deafness, is unusually frequent. In such communities, many of the outwardly normal persons will be heterozygous for the harmful gene, and more affected children will be born when these heterozygotes intermarry.

In our times, more and more small isolated communities are opened up through roads, buses, railways, and steamers. Let us consider the genetical consequences of this process. Suppose that a road has been built across a mountain pass between two formerly isolated small villages, Greenhill and Whitehill (Fig. 30). Both villages are among the unlucky small communities in which a harmful recessive gene demands its toll of disabled children in each generation; but, as would be expected, the recessive abnormalities are not the same in the two villages. In Greenhill, a few children each year are born blind because they are homozygous for a recessive gene *b;* in Whitehill, the defective children are deaf because they are homozygous for a recessive gene *d*. Among the normal-seeing adults in Greenhill, many are heterozygous for *b;* marriage between two of them may produce more blind children *bb*. In Whitehill, many normal-hearing adults are heterozygous for the gene *d* and may, when married with each other, have deaf children *dd*. After the new road has been constructed, a boy from Greenhill has an opportunity of meeting and marrying a girl from Whitehill, and vice versa. Now, even if the Greenhill boy and the Whitehill girl should both be heterozygous for the harmful gene carried in their community, *these genes are not the same*. Therefore, such a marriage will not result in children that are homozygous for *b* and blind or homozygous for *d* and deaf. Thus the first result of the road between the two villages is a decreased incidence of blind and deaf children. In general, any merging of small intermarrying communities into larger ones will lead to a decreased frequency of homozygotes for harmful recessive genes, and bicycles and cross-country buses have been called effective instruments of eugenics. We should, however, keep in mind that enlarging the size of the intermarrying group does not, like sterilization or voluntary abstention from procreation, eliminate harmful recessive genes. It only drives them underground in heterozygotes. In the long run, when the frequency of such a gene has increased sufficiently by repeated mutation, homozygotes will again be produced. Breaking the barriers between

FIG. 30.

The beneficial results of outbreeding.

hitherto isolated groups is therefore a process whose eugenically beneficial effects are only temporary; but, since mankind is still far from having reached the end of this process, we are likely to reap its benefit for many generations to come.

Negative eugenics would be helped greatly by methods for recognizing the effects of harmful genes in phenotypically normal individuals, be it of recessive genes or of dominant genes with incomplete penetrance. Most of the individuals whose cases we discussed in the previous chapter would benefit from such methods. Take the case of Edward on p. 77. As long as the possibility exists that he may carry the gene for retinoblastoma, he probably will anticipate the birth of his children with mixed feelings of joy and fear; if he could be assured that he was free of the dreaded gene his fear would vanish. Stephen and Mary (p. 79) would stand much better chances of adoption if the prospective foster parents could be assured that the children did not inherit the gene for Huntington's chorea. Bernard and Esther would find it much easier to decide whether or not to marry each other if they could be told whether or not they were free of the gene for amaurotic idiocy.

At present very few harmful genes can be spotted in healthy carriers, but the number of these genes is likely to increase as more refined methods are applied in the search for them. Some recessive genes which in homozygotes cause fatal anemias can be recognized in the blood picture of heterozygotes (Chap. 23). In principle, these anemias could be almost completely eliminated if heterozygotes refrained from marrying each other. In practice, this may not be easy because, for reasons to be discussed later, some populations have high numbers of heterozygotes. A special type of mental deficiency, phenylpyruvic idiocy (Chap. 23), is caused by a recessive gene in homozygous condition. Analysis of the blood and urine of patients has shown that affected persons are unable to utilize a constituent of protein, called "phenylalanine." In some way which is not yet understood, this metabolic abnormality affects the functioning of the brain. Heterozygotes have normal intelligence, but seem less able than normal persons to metabolize phenylalanine. In future, this may be developed into a test by which heterozygous relatives of patients can be recognized. It is possible that other genes producing mental deficiency or insanity may act by upsetting normal metabolic processes; if this is so, tests for the detection of heterozygotes may become feasible. Another device that promises to be useful for the spotting of genes affecting the brain is the electroencephalogram (EEG). This is a recording of the "brain waves" that result from the constantly occurring minute electrical currents in the human brain. Mentally abnormal persons often have abnormal EEG's. Attempts have been made to spot the presence of the gene for Huntington's chorea in the EEG of persons who, from their family history, may be suspected of carrying the gene but are not yet old enough to show symptoms of the disease. If these attempts should be successful, they would contribute greatly to the elimination of this exceedingly harmful gene. Most epileptics have abnormal EEG's, and this is also true for some of their healthy relatives. Quite probably, these are persons who have the genetical disposition for epilepsy and may transmit it to their children, although they themselves never suffered from fits. Even if this should turn out to be the right interpretation, it is doubtful whether the EEG will be used as a means against the spreading of genes for epilepsy. Although this disease certainly is hereditary in many cases, its penetrance is low. Many epileptics have healthy children, and this is even more likely to be true for those of their relatives whose only noticeable defect is an abnormal EEG. In Sweden, as has been mentioned before, persons suffering from the hereditary form of epilepsy are not allowed to marry, except when they have undergone sterilization. This law has recently been attacked by a Swedish geneticist, who points out that the chances for an epileptic to have epileptic children are not very high, that many epileptics are highly intelligent and socially valuable members of their community, well fitted to bring up children, and that they may carry valuable genes whose transmission will be prevented by the existing law.

I have dealt at some length with the case of epilepsy because it illustrates a typical dilemma of negative eugenics. Unless a condition is clearly undesirable and inherited in a well-understood way, like retinoblastoma or amaurotic idiocy, the geneticist will hesitate to enforce or even recommend negative eugenical measures, which infringe personal liberty, deprive individuals of the happiness of having children, and may carry the risk that desirable genes are lost in an attempt to guard against a possible transmission of undesirable ones. Many men of genius have been blind or deaf, epileptic or insane; if all of them had been prevented from having progeny, mankind would probably be poorer in some of the most precious genes.

This dilemma of negative eugenics is most acute in the case of curable hereditary diseases. In a sense, retinoblastoma is one of them; for timely operation or radiation treatment can save the lives of most of the victims of this gene. However, since the cure inevitably results in blindness in one or, more usually, both eyes, the geneticist will not feel much doubt that "cured" persons should be advised against having children. The situation is different for another type of hereditary blindness, juvenile cataract or cataract of the young. This is a disease that affects the lens of the eye and usually results in blindness at an early age. In most families, the disease is inherited as a dominant abnormality with high penetrance, and about half the children of affected persons are again affected. Cataract, however, is operable, and successfully operated persons can see well with suitable glasses and may become happy and useful members of society. Should one, then, prevent or dissuade them from having children, about half of whom again will have to undergo an operation and wear spectacles in order to see? In countries with sterilization laws, this question has been answered in the affirmative, and juvenile cataract is listed among the hereditary defects for which sterilization is recommended. There is no doubt that without such negative eugenical measures the frequency of the gene and with it the incidence of the defect will increase. This seems to have happened already for another defect which very often is hereditary. About 1 in 1,000 European infants nowadays are born with harelip and cleft palate; this is about twice as many as a hundred years ago. In part, this increase must be attributed to the fact that this malformation, which previously killed all of the more severely affected infants, can now be operated upon with such success that the expectation of life and marital chances of an affected person are hardly diminished.

Diabetes, too, has a hereditary basis, whose exact nature is still being investigated. Danish health statistics show that between 1927 and 1946 the number of diabetics in the population had increased more than threefold, and although improved methods of medical diagnosis and changes in diet and living standards certainly have contributed to this increase, part of it must probably be attributed to the increased life expectation of patients who, before the discovery of insulin in 1922, usually died young and childless. Many of these presumably carry the gene or genes for diabetes and will transmit them to some of their children. Since nobody would contemplate depriving diabetics of insulin treatment, should one then try to keep down the frequency of the genes for this disease by negative eugénic measures, or should one rest content with the consideration that, in a society that can make insulin, diabetics can live more or less normal lives?

These examples take us right into the center of a problem that has recently been much debated: Will the medical and social care that civilized societies extend to their weaker members result in genetical deterioration? The answer to this question will depend on the viewpoint of the observer. If he takes a strictly biological view, he will consider mankind as just another one of the thousands of species whose fitness is defined by their reproductive capacity. Since, on this definition, a diabetic or an idiot with five children is fitter than a childless man or woman of exceptional health and intelligence, such an observer will make light of the possible dangers that the care for the present generation may create for the coming ones. But most of us will feel that in the life of human individuals and societies quality counts for more than quantity. What we ask, therefore, is this: Will our medical and social services in the long run create a majority of individuals who, because of some inherited defect, are not able to lead full and satisfactory lives? Will the progress of human society become more and more impeded by excessive expenditure of money and effort in the service of the physically and mentally unfit? Put like this, the problem is at least amenable to discussion, although the answer will necessarily remain subjective to the extent that personal judgment decides what is to be considered a satisfactory individual life or a tolerable social burden.

Opinions would, indeed, not differ greatly if we looked at the matter exclusively from the viewpoint of what are *un*desirable genes, that is, from the viewpoint of negative eugenics. Nobody can doubt that it is better to be born with a normally closed palate than to acquire one through operation in infancy; to see with one's own eyes than through cataract lenses; to be independent of drugs than to survive only with the aid of insulin. The picture of a future society in which everyone has to undergo an operation in infancy, has to wear glasses, use a hearing aid, keep a strict diet, and take a number of different drugs can hardly appeal to the imagination. Thus if our only concern were to get rid of undesirable genes we would feel that our efforts for the well-being of our contemporaries endanger the heritage of future generations, and we would try our best to keep this danger low by strict measures of negative eugenics. But we must not lose sight of the fact that every human being carries tens of thousands of genes, some good, others bad, and that for the future of mankind it is at least as important to preserve the good genes—or even to increase their frequency—as to get rid of the bad ones. The care of the good genes is the domain of positive eugenics. We have already seen in the case of epilepsy how considerations of positive and negative eugenics have to be balanced against each other in genetic counseling.

POSITIVE EUGENICS

There have been hardly any attempts at carrying out a program of positive eugenics, and for good reasons. We still lack the main requirements for such a program, namely, (a) clearly defined aims, (b) effective methods, and (c) knowledge of the genetics of desirable human traits. The last requirement is least important. Plant and animal breeding have achieved success without detailed knowledge of the inheritance of economically important characters like grain or egg yield, meat quality or hardiness. The main methods of plant and animal breeding are controlled matings and selection; neither can be used in human societies without an intolerable infringement of individual liberty. Other methods will become available in time. One, artificial insemination, is already used in special cases. Others, like the controlled union of a selected ovum with a selected sperm and "foster rearing" of the resulting embryo by a woman, are on the horizon. Still others, like "gene transplantation" (see Chap. 25) are as yet in the faraway future. Doubtless these methods will meet with much resistance of an emotional origin; but, apart from the possibility that this resistance may not stand up to rational arguments, experience has abundantly shown that any new technique which becomes available will eventually be put to use. It is therefore necessary to be prepared for the future and to define the aims of positive eugenics. To do this we have to decide what are desirable traits in man.

At first sight it might look as though agreement on this point would be impossible, but this seems exaggerated pessimism. It is true that no two persons are likely to have exactly the same image of the ideal human type, but this is not necessarily a bad starting point for discussion. Human society requires many different talents and temperaments, and variety among human beings is a precious gift which should be preserved as far as is compatible with a few essentially and fundamentally desirable traits. To achieve agreement on these traits does not seem too difficult either. Health will certainly be among them, although it will not rank highest. It seems almost self-evident that top rank should be accorded those traits which have made man into the ruling species on earth: intelligence, inventiveness, imagination, coupled with will power and perseverance. But by themselves these qualities cannot suffice. They can attain full value only through co-operation, and without co-operation on a world-wide scale they will eventually lead to the destruction of mankind. Thus among the essentially desirable human traits are also those required for profitable co-operation, such as fairness, kindness, tolerance, and sympathy. Finally, the abilities for the creation and appreciation of spiritual values, for instance the visual arts, arose early in human evolution and, for many among us, still give human life its unique value. Few would disagree that these abilities are among the desirable human traits.

Some may object that most of these desirable human qualities are the result of education and tradition rather than heredity. There is much truth in this objection, for in our species physical heredity by way of genes has become supplemented and often greatly surpassed in importance by what we might call cultural heredity. Yet, as we shall see in Chapter 16, there are hardly any human traits that do not in some degree depend on heredity, and to the extent that this holds good they will respond to eugenical measures. The surest way to recognize hereditary differences in desirable qualities is to give all individuals the best possible environmental conditions, including a good education, so that no hereditary gifts are suppressed by unfavorable circumstances.

I do not wish to leave the impression that there will not be any major disagreements about the aims of positive eugenics. Disagreement is most likely to arise in regard to the desirable over-all genetical structure of humanity. Most of us probably wish that in future generations more and more individuals will partake of what we consider essentially desirable human qualities. But there will also be those who dream of a brave new world in which humanity is divided into genetically different castes: a small minority of high intelligence, strong will power and, perhaps, ability to enjoy spiritual values, and a majority of mentally inferior and submissive individuals, bred and trained to keep the machinery of society going through their various services, including the breeding of an adequate supply of their own kind. For many persons, including myself, this is an entirely abhorrent picture. We must hope that when effective means for positive eugenics become available they will be controlled by wise and humane individuals or groups.

It may be that in the near future we shall see how mankind acquits itself in a test case of minor importance: the control of the proportions in which boys and girls are being born, which may soon become possible. For an understanding of this possibility we shall have to look at the way in which sex is determined, and this we shall do in the next chapter.

CHAPTER 14 *"It's a Boy"*

YOU MAY REMEMBER the photograph of the chromosomes in a cell of Drosophila melanogaster (Plate II, 3). There are four pairs of them. One pair consists of two medium-sized rod-shaped chromosomes, two consist of long chromosomes which usually assume the form of the letter V, and one pair consists of small dot-like

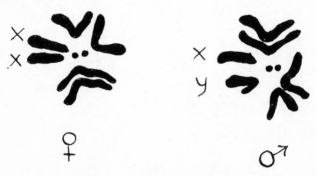

FIG. 31.
The chromosomes in Drosophila males and females.

chromosomes. This is the typical picture of the chromosomes in a female cell. In Fig. 31 (left) it has been redrawn in comparison with the chromosomes in a male cell (right). The difference is evident. Instead of two rod-shaped chromosomes, the male has only one; the partner chromosome has been replaced by one of a different shape, looking somewhat like a shepherd's crook. The rod-shaped

100

chromosome is called X; its bent partner in the male is called Y. Every Drosophila female has two X chromosomes, every male has one X and one Y. These chromosomes are therefore called "sex chromosomes." The remaining three chromosome pairs, which look the same in both sexes, are called "autosomes."

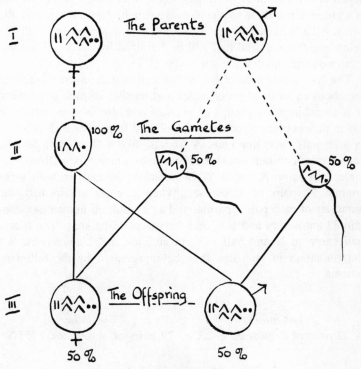

FIG. 32.
Sex determination in Drosophila.

Figure 32 shows diagrammatically how the sex of the offspring is determined in Drosophila. In row I you see once more the chromosomes in the two parents. When gametes are formed, the sex chromosomes behave like every other chromosome pair (Chap. 3): the two members separate and go into opposite gametes. As a result, all ova receive one X chromosome, while the spermatozoa are of two types: half of them carry an X, and half carry a Y. In addition, each gamete contains one member of each pair of autosomes (II). When a Drosophila female mates, she stores a large number of spermatozoa in a special container that opens into the passage through which the egg reaches the outside. Every time an egg is laid, the female releases some of the stored spermatozoa, and one of them fertilizes the egg. Whether the successful spermatozoon belongs to the X-bearing or to the Y-bearing class is a matter of chance. Since these two classes are equally large, about half the ova will be fertilized by an X-bearing spermatozoon and will develop into females, and half will be fertilized by a Y-bearing spermatozoon and will develop into males (III).

The X-Y mechanism of sex determination thus ensures that there are about equal numbers of males and females in each generation. It is found in many groups of animals and also in some plants in which the sexes are separate, as in willows. In particular, it is found in mammals, including man. A woman, like a Drosophila female, carries two X chromosomes in all her cells; a man, like a Drosophila male, carries an X and a Y. In addition, the cells in both sexes contain 22 pairs of autosomes. When gametes are formed, the members of each pair separate, and as a result all human ova contain 22 autosomes and 1 X, and the spermatozoa are of two types: half carry an X and half a Y, in addition to 22 autosomes. Sex determination in man can thus be represented by the following scheme:

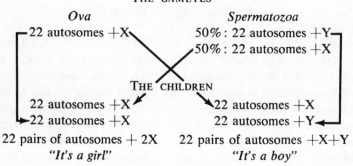

THE PARENTS

The mother   *The father*
22 pairs of autosomes + 2X   22 pairs of autosomes +X+Y

THE GAMETES

Ova   *Spermatozoa*
22 autosomes +X   50% : 22 autosomes +Y
                         50% : 22 autosomes +X

THE CHILDREN

22 autosomes +X   22 autosomes +X
22 autosomes +X   22 autosomes +Y
22 pairs of autosomes + 2X   22 pairs of autosomes +X+Y
"It's a girl"   *"It's a boy"*

This mechanism has two important features:

(1) The decisive factor in human sex determination is the spermatozoon. The ovum is neutral; whether it develops into a girl or a boy depends upon whether it is fertilized by an X-bearing or a Y-bearing spermatozoon.

(2) Sex is determined at the moment of conception. Nothing done after this can change the genetical sex of the child. Once a woman carries a female embryo, no amount of listening to military marches or looking at pictures of brawny athletes will make her give birth to a boy.

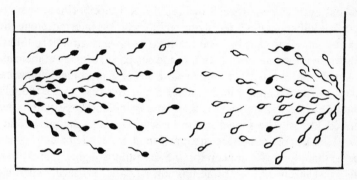

FIG. 33.
Separation of X- and Y-bearing spermatozoa by means of
an electric current.

It follows that if one wants to control the sex of a prospective child one has to act on the spermatozoa before fertilization. There have been promising attempts at separating spermatozoa outside the body by electrical means (Fig. 33). When an electrical current was sent through a fluid in which spermatozoa of a rabbit were suspended, these began to move tail foremost toward the two poles. When the spermatozoa were subsequently used for artificial insemination, those collected near the positive pole produced more females than males, those collected near the negative pole more males than females. Apparently, X-bearing spermatozoa had tended to move toward the positive, Y-bearing spermatozoa toward the negative pole. This method might in time be developed for use in the artificial insemination of cattle, where control over the ratio of heifers to bullocks born would be of great value. For natural insemination, the problem will have to be approached in a different way. Claims to influence the sex of the child by chemicals introduced into the seminal fluid have so far not stood up to critical tests. It is, however, entirely possible that an effective method will eventually be worked out. If so, mankind will have an opportunity for showing whether it can make wise use of this new power over nature or whether lack of foresight and co-operation will result in alternate gluts of bachelors and spinsters.

That even without special devices the two types of human spermatozoa differ in their fertilizing ability can be inferred from the sex ratio at birth, that is, from the ratio of boys to girls born. Since this ratio reflects the segregation of the sex chromosomes at meiosis, it should be exactly 1:1 in the absence of disturbing influences. Actually, it is slightly but definitely larger. At first it was thought that this was due to more girls than boys dying during gestation, but this could easily be shown not to be true; for even among miscarriages and abortions there are more males than females. It thus seems that already at conception the sex ratio is higher than 1, and this must mean that for some unknown reason Y-bearing spermatozoa have a better chance of fertilizing ova than X-bearing ones.

A distinction has to be made between sex determination and sex differentiation. Sex determination is a mechanism by which chromosomes are distributed in accordance with Mendel's first law. Sex differentiation is the chain of developmental processes by which the genetically determined sex becomes translated into characteristic structures, functions, and behavior patterns. Sex determination, as we saw, is completed at conception. Sex differentiation continues throughout embryonic development, childhood, and adolescence. Disturbing factors, in particular hormones, may make it deviate from its normal course, so that the genetical sex cannot become fully expressed or may even assume some features of the opposite sex. A well-known example occurs in cattle. When a cow gives birth to twins of unlike sex, the male is normal, but the female very often is a sterile "freemartin," whose internal sex organs are halfway between male and female in structure. A freemartin starts life as a genetical female, but its sex differentiation is diverted from its normal course by male hormones produced in the twin embryo and carried into the female through a connection between the embryonic blood vessels. Freemartins are known only in cattle; in particular they do not occur in the human species, where fusion between the blood vessels of twin embryos of unlike sex is rare. Twin sisters of boys are sexually normal and fertile. Yet intersexes, that is, individuals who do not belong clearly to one or the other

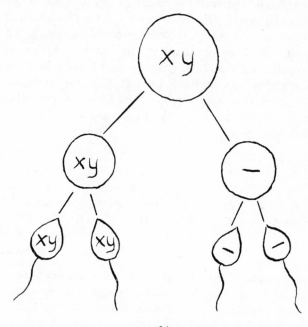

FIG. 34.
Nondisjunction.

sex, are also found in man. Clinically, various types of intersexuality can be distinguished. Some of them may be due to hormonal disturbances; quite recently it has been found that some are caused by abnormal chromosome constitutions. Certain outwardly male intersexes have two X chromosomes like a woman, but in addition one Y chromosome like a man. Certain outwardly female intersexes have only one X chromosome like a man, but lack a Y chromosome.

It is not difficult to imagine how these abnormalities of chromosome constitution have arisen. One possibility is outlined in Fig. 34. In one of the gamete-forming cells of a man the sex chromosomes have failed to separate at meiosis. As a result, both of them have been included into the same cell and have given rise to two spermatozoa that, in addition to the normal 22 autosomes, carry both an X and a Y. The other two spermatozoa have received no sex chromosome and carry only autosomes. When one of these abnormal spermatozoa fertilizes a normal, X-bearing ovum, the embryo will contain either two X chromosomes plus a Y (XXY) or one X chromosome by itself (X0). Such errors of meiosis, called nondisjunction,* have been extensively studied in lower organisms. In Drosophila, XXY and X0 types are well known; in the mouse, both types have recently been detected. Curiously enough, these abnormal sex-chromosome constitutions have different effects on the sexual development of humans, mice and flies. This is shown in the following table:

	XY	XX	XXY	X0
Man	♂	♀	male-type intersex	female-type intersex
Mouse	♂	♀	sterile male	fertile ♀
Drosophila	♂	♀	fertile ♀	sterile ♂ (not otherwise intersexual)

It can be seen from this table that the Y chromosome, which plays an important role in the sex determination of humans and mice, has no significance for that of Drosophila. XXY ♀ ♀ are perfectly normal and fertile, and X0 ♂ ♂ are normal in every respect, even to the point of producing abundant and normally formed sperm. The only contribution of the Y chromosome to the physiology of sex (not to its determination) is that it carries genes that are required for making the spermatozoa motile. In several groups of organisms, for instance, grasshoppers, a Y chromosome

---

* Nondisjunction appears to be responsible also for a special type of feeble-mindedness, Mongolian idiocy. Mongolian idiots have one small autosome in triplicate, instead of—as is normal—in duplicate. Thus either the ovum or the sperm producing a Mongolian idiot must have contained both members of this particular pair of autosomes. With modern methods of chromosome counting in humans, more abnormalities may be found to be due to nondisjunction, resulting in abnormal chromosome constitutions.

is missing altogether, and sex is determined wholly by the presence of either one or two X chromosomes.

There is, a priori, no reason why the female should be XX, the

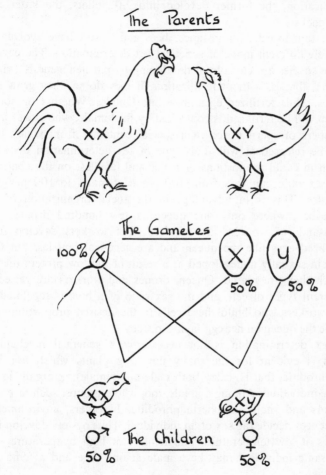

FIG. 35.
Sex determination in the fowl.

male XY or X0, instead of the other way round. In fact, several groups of animals have evolved the latter type of sex determination, in which the male is XX and the female XY or X0. In particular, this is so for birds. Figure 35 shows sex determination in the fowl.

The cock is XX, and all spermatozoa carry an X chromosome. The hen is X0 and produces two types of ova in equal proportion: those without a sex chromosome and those carrying an X. After fertilization, the former develop into X0 pullets, the latter into XX cocks.

Certain insects, for instance, bees and wasps, have evolved an entirely different mode of genetical sex determination. The eggs of these species are capable of developing by parthenogenesis (virgin birth), that is, without fertilization. If they do so, they grow into males, while fertilized eggs grow into females. Whether or not an ovum will be fertilized is controlled by the female, who stores large numbers of spermatozoa in a special container from which they can be released at will. This type of sex determination does not result in equal proportions of males and females; on the contrary, the sex ratio can vary from 100 per cent males to 100 per cent females. This is of advantage in the social organization of the honeybee, where only one queen, a few hundred drones, and thousands of workers are required. The workers develop from fertilized eggs like the queen and are genetical females, but they remain sexually undeveloped as a result of the low protein diet on which they are reared. Queen, drones and workers are raised in different types of cell, and the sex ratio of a hive is regulated by the workers who build these cells in the desired proportions and guide the queen on her egg-laying journey.

Sex determination is not necessarily a genetical mechanism. This is evident for the many flowering plants which are hermaphroditic, that is, carry both male and female sex organs in the same individual. Among animals, too, whole groups, such as earthworms and snails, are hermaphroditic. In others, environmental influences decide the sex of an individual. Thus oysters develop into males at low temperature, into females at high temperature, and the same individual may be a male at one time and a female at another.

CHAPTER 15 *"Father's Girl, Mother's Boy"*

IT IS AN old belief that boys take after their mother, girls after their father. As far as biological—as distinct from educational—inheritance is concerned, this is true only for a few special traits and even for those only to a very limited extent. These traits are called sex-linked.

When, during the evolution of certain groups of organisms, one pair of chromosomes became specialized into vehicles of sex-determining genes, other genes not related to sex often happened to be "trapped" in these chromosomes. In most species, the Y chromosome carries few, if any, genes not concerned with sex determination and, as we have seen, it may not even carry those. The term "sex-linked" therefore refers to genes in the X chromosome without partner genes in the Y. The number of sex-linked genes varies greatly between species. In Drosophila melanogaster, the X chromosome forms about one fifth of the whole chromosome material in the female and somewhat less in the male (Fig. 31); it carries many sex-linked genes which affect the most varied characters: size and color of body, size and shape of wings, size, shape, structure and color of eyes, and so on. Only a few sex-linked genes are known in the mouse, where the genetic material is distributed over 38 autosomes and one or two X chromosomes. Several sex-linked genes have been found in man.

Sex-linked genes form the one major exception to the rule that in sexually produced organisms all genes occur in pairs; for they are without partner genes in all XY individuals, such as Drosophila males, men, or hens. This has an important consequence. XY individuals cannot be heterozygous for sex-linked genes. They cannot, therefore, carry recessive sex-linked genes masked by their normal alleles, and every sex-linked gene—whether dominant or recessive—manifests itself in the XY sex. Red-green color blind-

FIG. 36.
Transmission of the sex chromosomes from parents to children.

ness in man is caused by a recessive sex-linked gene, which we may call *cb*. A woman, with two X chromosomes, may be genotypically *cb cb* and phenotypically color-blind, or $++$ and normal-seeing, or *cb* $+$ and normal-seeing; a man, with one X chromosome, can only be *cb* and color-blind, or $+$ and normal-seeing. In the domestic fowl, silver (a certain type of white plumage) and gold (brown) are a pair of sex-linked genes, silver (*S*) being dominant over gold (*s*). A male, being XX, may be genotypically *SS* and phenotypically silver, *ss* and gold, or *Ss* and silver; a hen, with one X chromosome, can only be *S* and silver or *s* and gold.

In their transmission from parents to offspring, sex-linked genes willy-nilly have to follow the sex-determining genes on the X. In order to understand the results of this type of transmission, let us look at the facts discussed in Chapter 14 from a slightly different angle. Figure 36 shows how the sex chromosomes are transmitted in a family consisting of mother, father, son, and daughter.

The mother.

She has two X chromosomes. She transmits one of these to all her children, sons as well as daughters. Half the children will inherit one of the X chromosomes, half will inherit the other.

The father.

He has one X and one Y chromosome. He transmits his X chromosome to *all* his daughters, his Y chromosome to *all* his sons. He never transmits an X chromosome to a son for, according to Mendel's first law, each spermatozoon carries either the X or the Y, not both (except in the rare and abnormal cases of nondisjunction; see p. 106).

The daughter.

She has two X chromosomes. She has inherited one of them from her mother, the other one from her father, in the same way as she has inherited one member of each pair of autosomes from one of her two parents. Genetically, therefore, she has inherited exactly half her genes from each of her parents and is as much her mother's as her father's daughter.

The son.

He has an X and a Y chromosome. He has inherited his X from his mother, his Y from his father. According to Mendel's first law, he inherits only one sex chromosome from each of his parents; he cannot, therefore, inherit an X from his father. Thus all his sex-linked genes come from his mother's side, and in respect to these genes—but only in respect to them—he is his mother's and not his father's boy.

A few examples will illustrate the characteristic features of sex-linked inheritance in man:

(1) *A ricket-like bone abnormality.* Figure 37 shows part of the pedigree of an American family many members of which were afflicted with severe disturbances of bone development, which outwardly resembled those produced by rickets. However—unlike rickets—the disease did not respond to treatment with vitamin D. At first glance it is obvious that the disease in this family is caused by a dominant gene. There is no skipping of generations; every affected child has an affected parent. Moreover, as

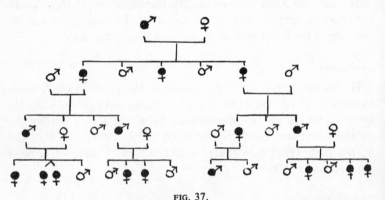

FIG. 37.
Transmission of a ricket-like disturbance in bone development.

would be expected if the affected persons are heterozygous, about half their children are healthy. If now we compare this pedigree with others of dominant abnormalities, for instance, Huntington's chorea (Fig. 27), we notice that it differs from them in a remarkable way. All the daughters and none of the sons of affected men are affected, while affected women have both affected and healthy sons and daughters. Figure 36 shows that this is exactly what must be expected if the harmful dominant gene is carried on the X chromosome.

(2) *Red-green color blindness.* This abnormality, as has already been mentioned, is due to the action of a recessive sex-linked gene. Such a gene is transmitted in exactly the same way as a dominant sex-linked gene; but the transmission of the observable abnormality is different, because heterozygous women are

phenotypically normal. Figure 38 shows how the same geno-typical pedigree of a sex-linked gene (I) can give rise to two quite different family histories depending upon whether the gene is dominant (II) like that for severe rickets or recessive (III) like that for red-green blindness. The striking feature of the recessive pedigree (III) lies in the fact that an affected man transmits the abnormality through his outwardly normal daughters to some of his grandsons, while a normal man does not transmit it at all. Thus a woman transmits color blindness to her sons no matter whom she marries. If she is heterozygous—and normal-sighted—about half her sons will be color-blind; if she is homozygous and herself color-blind, all her sons will be affected. No woman—either heterozygous or homozygous—can have color-blind daughters by a normal-sighted man.

Color-blind women are much rarer than color-blind men. This is easily understood if we consider that any man who carries the *cb* gene on his one X chromosome is color-blind, while a woman needs to carry the gene on both her X chromosomes in order to show its effect. Since, therefore, color-blind women must have inherited the gene from both parents, they must have a color-blind father (*cb*Y) as well as a mother who is at least heterozygous for the gene (*cb*+). When a color-blind woman (*cb cb*) marries a normal-seeing man (+Y), her sons will be color-blind (*cb*Y) and her daughters normal-seeing (*cb*+). This, therefore, is one of the rare instances of "crisscross inheritance" or "father's girl, mother's boy." You see that it requires special conditions, namely, a sex-linked recessive gene for which the mother is homozygous while the father has the dominant normal allele.

(3) *Hemophilia* (Bleeder disease). Bleeders are persons whose blood takes an excessively long time to clot when exposed to air, so that even minor wounds or operations result in dangerous loss of blood. The most frequent form of this disease is caused by a sex-linked recessive gene and follows the same type of inheritance as red-green color blindness. In particular, a healthy man cannot carry the gene. This fact has been of importance in the British royal family. Queen Victoria was heterozygous for the hemophilia gene, presumably as the result of a mutation in one of her parents. She had one hemophilic son and two heterozygous daughters, who carried the gene into the then reigning houses of Spain and Russia,

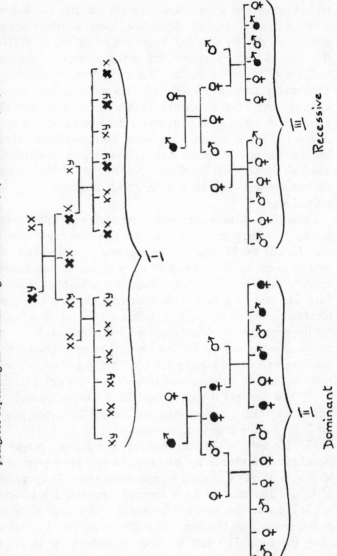

FIG. 38.

Transmission of a sex-linked gene. The same type of transmission (I) results in different pedigrees depending on whether the gene is dominant (II) or recessive (III).

where it affected several of her grandsons and great-grandsons. The British monarchy, however, was carried on by a healthy son, Edward VII, so that it no longer carries this harmful gene.

Already in the early centuries A.D., the Jews had noticed the fatal effect of hemophilia on circumcised boys. Rules laid down in the Talmud show that their originators had clearly understood the facts, although not the causes, of sex-linked inheritance. Thus a boy was not to be circumcised if his mother had previously lost two boys at circumcision, even if she had meanwhile married another man. On the contrary, if a man had previously lost two sons at circumcision, his sons by a different wife had still to be circumcised. This shows realization of the fact that a boy inherits the disease from his mother and not from his father.

Until recently there were no known cases of women suffering from sex-linked hemophilia. This was thought to be due to the rarity of the type of marriage in which hemophilic women might be produced (hemophilic man and heterozygous woman). In dogs, where the same disease is caused by a sex-linked recessive gene, hemophilic bitches have occurred in litters from hemophilic males and carrier females. At least one well-authenticated case of a homozygous hemophilic woman is now known.

From the viewpoint of negative eugenics, sex-linked recessive genes occupy an intermediate position between ordinary (autosomal) recessive and dominant genes. In women, a sex-linked recessive gene may be carried hidden like any other recessive gene; in men, it always manifests itself, as though it were a dominant gene. Attempts to reduce the frequency of harmful sex-linked recessives in a human population are, therefore, less futile than negative eugenic measures against harmful autosomal recessives (p. 87).

Finally, let us look at a few cases of sex-linked inheritance in domestic animals. The case of hemophilia in dogs has already been mentioned. In cats, yellow and black are due to a pair of sex-linked allelomorphs which in the heterozygote give the well-known tortoise-shell pattern. Since in cats, as in all mammals, the ♂ is the XY sex, only females can be heterozygous with tortoise-shell fur; the very rare exceptional tortoise-shell toms are sterile and presumably XXY in genotype (cf. 106). Figure 39 illustrates the inheritance of black (B) and yellow (b) in the cat. A tortoise-

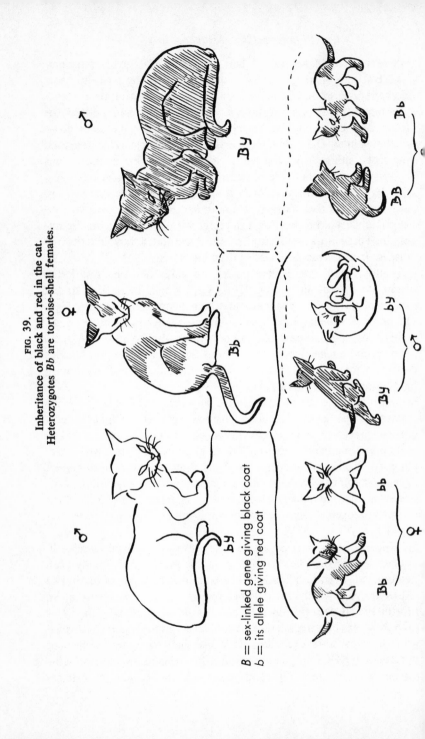

FIG. 39.
Inheritance of black and red in the cat.
Heterozygotes *Bb* are tortoise-shell females.

B = sex-linked gene giving black coat
b = its allele giving red coat

shell (*Bb*) cat has both black (*BY*) and yellow (*bY*) sons by any male. Her daughters by a black male are black (*BB*) and tortoise-shell (*Bb*); those by a yellow male are yellow (*bb*) and tortoise-shell (*Bb*). Thus, whether a female kitten is black or yellow depends on the genotype of both its father and mother; whether a male kitten is black or yellow depends only on the mother's genotype.

In the domestic fowl, crisscross inheritance can be used to facilitate the sexing of newly hatched chicks. We have seen that crisscross inheritance occurs when a woman is homozygous for a sex-linked recessive gene for which the man carries the dominant allele. In birds, where the male is XX and the female XO, the conditions for crisscross inheritance are the opposite: the cock must be homozygous for a sex-linked recessive gene for which the hen carries the normal allele. A pair of genes that can be used for the purpose are silver (*S,* dominant) and gold (*s,* recessive) (Fig. 40). A gold male (*ss,* for instance, a Brown Leghorn) crossed with a silver female (*SY* for instance, a White Wyandotte), produces gold pullets (*sY*) and silver cockerels (*Ss*). Gold and silver are easily distinguished in the down plumage and allow the poultry breeder to dispense with the services of an expert for the difficult task of sexing young chicks.

A different method, which does not require crossing between different strains, makes use of the sex-linked gene for barring. This gene produces white stripes on adult black plumage and white patches in the down plumage. In males with two genes for barring the stripes are wider than in females with only one such gene, and a similar difference is found in the down plumage (Plate IV). Introduction of the barring gene into a number of breeds has resulted in the so-called "autosexing" breeds, such as the Cambar, the Ancobar, the Legbar.

It would be erroneous to assume the action of a sex-linked gene wherever the sexes differ in the frequency of an inherited trait. Baldness not due to illness occurs much more frequently in men than in women; it is caused by a dominant gene which—unlike the sex-linked genes—can be transmitted from father to son. Women who inherit and transmit this gene are rarely bald. Apparently, the female constitution provides a less favorable background for the manifestation of the gene than the male one. Similarly, gout is a disease that affects mainly men, but does not follow a sex-linked type of inheritance. The essential action of the responsible gene is to increase the content of uric acid in the blood; since men normally

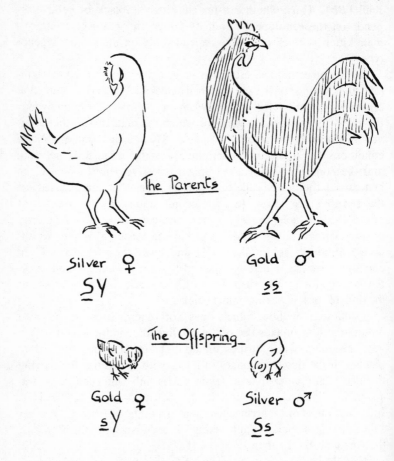

The Parents

Silver ♀
S̲Y

Gold ♂
s̲s̲

The Offspring

Gold ♀
s̲Y

Silver ♂
S̲s̲

FIG. 40.
Sexing young chicks by means of a pair of sex-linked genes.

carry more uric acid in their blood than women, the excess produced by the action of this gene is more likely to make them manifestly ill. Genes that, without being sex-linked, manifest themselves more readily in one sex than in the other are called "sex-influenced." Certain genes manifest themselves exclusively in one sex, and these are called "sex-limited." Genes for milk yield in cattle or egg yield in poultry belong in this class; for, although they can be transmitted by males, they cannot be recognized in them.

The consideration of sex-influenced and sex-limited genes has led us away from problems of gene transmission to problems of gene effects. We have seen that the effect of a gene may be dependent on the physiological background in which it is called upon to act. In the following chapter we shall deal more fully with the manner in which gene effects may be influenced by environment in every sense, from climate and education to the presence of other genes in the same nucleus.

CHAPTER **16**   *Nature and Nurture*

> As round the sun when first you saw his light
> In solemn order planets stood arrayed,
> So was implanted in you for a guide
> The law that ever since you have obeyed.
> Once sybils sang and wise men prophesied:
> "This you must be, this you cannot evade."
> And neither time nor force destroys the mould
> In which Life's forms are coined as they unfold.
>
> GOETHE

ACCORDING TO A very old superstition, character and fate of an individual are determined by the constellation of the planets at the hour of his birth. Toward the end of the previous century, when man became increasingly aware of the role played by heredity in the formation of body and mind, he tended to allot to hereditary influences the role that astrology had alloted to the stars. In the writings of authors like Zola and Ibsen the moment of conception, when the constellation of genes is formed, assumes the same sinister significance that the moment of birth carries for the astrologer.

Modern medicine, psychology, and educational philosophy emphasize, on the contrary, the role of environment in the development of the individual. Many people reconcile these two viewpoints by classifying all traits into hereditary and nonhereditary ones. The latter are thought to be formed under the influence of outside agencies; the former are considered an inescapable doom or an inalienable possession. Thus for many medical practitioners a disease is either hereditary, in which case not much can be done about it, or nonhereditary, in which case it offers hope of successful prevention and treatment. We have already seen that this distinction is not valid, and that many inherited diseases can be successfully treated.

Again, some people believe that intelligence is hereditary, others believe that it is not. The latter hold that all men would be able to reach the same level of intelligence if they were given the same educational opportunities. The former believe that children who have inherited genes for good intelligence will develop into intellectually superior persons even without much education, while children who have not been so lucky in their genes will fail to profit even from an excellent education.

The same two schools of thought are found in regard to criminality. Some consider criminal tendencies as an inherited doom from which there is no escape. A well-known book bears the title *Crime as Destiny*. The opposite view has been expressed by a retired British police officer who wrote in his autobiography: "We must be rid of the notion of the criminal as an hereditary type; he is you or I or the man next door."

To the geneticist, questions like "Is criminality inherited? Is cancer a hereditary disease? Is intelligence the result of education?" make no sense. They presuppose an antithesis which he knows to be wrong, the antithesis between heredity and environment, between "nature and nurture" (Galton, 1874). Every trait, normal or abnormal, is the result of developmental processes, and these are controlled by genes as well as environment. It is true that the relative contributions of heredity and environment to any particular trait differ widely, but few traits are determined entirely by heredity, even fewer by environment. A bullet wound is caused by an outside agency, but the wounded person may have been involved in a brawl through his aggressive disposition, which at least in part may be inherited. Moreover, the effects of the wound on his general health and spirit and the speed of recuperation depend on his constitution, and this is partly hereditary. At the other end of the nature-nurture scale we have a number of traits that, at least under present conditions, are wholly gene-determined, such as blood groups, eye color, and diseases like Huntington's chorea. For some of these, environmental remedies may be found in the future; for others, this may not be possible because the connection between the gene and its observed effect is too direct for human interference. Between these extremes lies the vast majority of characters that are due to an interplay between genes and environment.

The first environment of a mammal is its mother's womb. We have already met several instances of interaction between prenatal environment and the genes of the embryo. An Rh-positive child develops normally in an Rh-positive mother but may be severely affected in an Rh-negative one. A genetically female calf may develop into a sterile freemartin because the action of its sex genes has been overriden by hormones from a male twin embryo. A further example is shown in Fig. 41. In a cross between large Shire horses and small Shetland ponies, the size of the foal depends on the way in which the cross has been made. A Shetland mare mated to a Shire stallion produces a smaller foal than a Shire mare mated to a Shetland stallion. Genetically, the two foals have the same mixture of size-determining genes (sex-linked genes play no role in this case); but only in the womb of the large Shire mare can these genes take full effect.

Once the animal is born, new environmental influences are brought to bear on it and affect the action of its genes. Whether a cow is a good milker depends at least as much on the care and food it receives as on its genes. Some people have to diet in order not to put on too much weight; others can gorge themselves with sweets without losing their slim figures. The same interplay of heredity and environment occurs in regard to more specific characters. Rabbits that are homozygous for a certain recessive gene form yellow fat from a substance contained in green food. From the consumer's point of view, yellow fat is an undesirable gene effect. A rabbit breeder whose stock happens to carry the gene for yellow fat can completely mask its action by feeding his animals mash without greens.

Many genes depend on temperature for their action. The Himalayan pattern in the rabbit (Chap. 10, Fig. 22) is caused by a gene that allows the formation of pigment only at low temperature. Consequently, only the most exposed parts of the body are colored. When an area on the back or flank is plucked and the animal is kept cold, the new hair grows out black and forms a dark patch

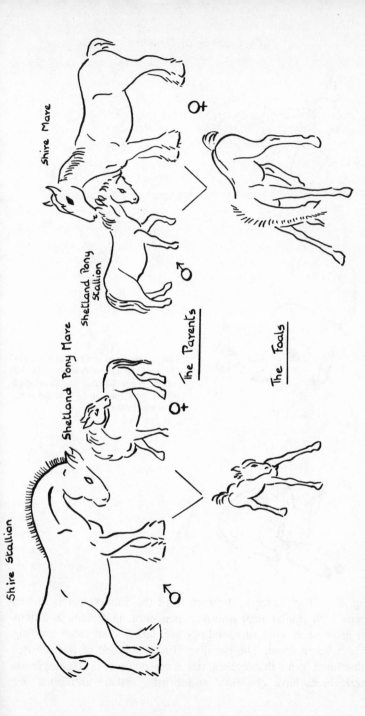

Shire Stallion

Shetland Pony Mare ♀

♂

Shire Mare

Shetland Pony Stallion ♂

♀

The Parents

The Foals

FIG. 41.

The influence of different prenatal environments on the same genotype. Reciprocal crosses between Shetland and Shire horses.

FIG. 42.
The influence of temperature on the effect of the Himalayan gene in the rabbit. A black patch has developed where new hair in a plucked area grew out in the cold.

(Fig. 42). The characteristic pattern of the Siamese cat is due to a gene with similar temperature dependence, and Siamese kittens that grow up in cold surroundings are darker than those growing up in a warm room. The peculiar "Frizzle" breed of fowl carries a dominant gene that causes the feathers to curl. Homozygous Frizzle birds have abnormal and brittle feathers and often are almost completely naked. When such a naked bird was given a woolen coat it developed plumage all over its body.

The life of green plants depends on light; for they make nutrients from the air by means of green chlorophyll, and this process occurs only in the light. Moreover, most plants cannot form chlorophyll in the dark. Many genes are required for the formation of chlorophyll; when one of them is missing or deficient the seedling is an albino without chlorophyll and dies of starvation (Chap. 4, Fig. 4). Even a seedling that possesses all necessary genes for chlorophyll formation will not become green without light. Thus the same phenotype—a white seedling which dies—may be due either to a defective genotype (Fig. 43 C) or a defective environment (Fig. 43 A).

Some plants flower only when the days are sufficiently long; such plants flower well in the long summer days of countries far away from the equator. Other plants, on the contrary, require the short days of near equatorial countries for flowering. The difference between these two classes of plants is genetically determined, and the phenotype "flowering plant" is due to an interaction between these genes and the length of the days (Fig. 44).

Most genes, thus, do not produce stereotyped effects but merely determine the way in which the organism reacts to its environment. This is true also for genes that cause abnormality or disease in man. We have seen in Chapter 12 that many of these genes are incompletely penetrant, that is, they often fail to show up in a person who genotypically carries the potentiality to develop the disease. In these cases environmental conditions, usually still unknown to medicine, prevent the expression of harmful genes. Conversely, genotypical differences often determine the response to environmental causes of disease.

Infectious diseases clearly have an environmental cause. There can be no infectious disease without invasion of the body by a germ. But whether an infection will result in a slight or severe illness or in no illness at all, depends on a variety of circumstances, such as general health at the time of an epidemic, or immunity due to a previous, often unnoticed, slight infection by the same type of germ. In addition, genotypical differences in susceptibility often play a role. As early as 1898 a physician in Maine noticed that infantile paralysis (poliomyelitis), which then was a new,

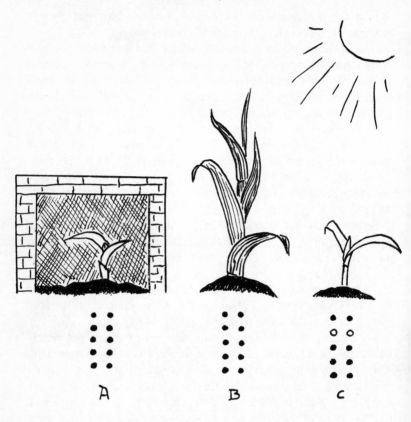

● = Normal genes for chlorophyll formation
○ = Mutated gene which prevents chlorophyll
          formation

FIG. 43.
The same character (absence of chlorophyll) developed as a result
of an environmental (A) or a genic (C) deficiency. Only 5 pairs for
chlorophyll formation have been shown; in reality there are many
more.

hardly known disease, tended to strike children within the same
family. In 1943 a high school teacher in McDowell County, West
Virginia, collected all cases of crippling from infantile paralysis
that had occurred in this region over fifty years. All were found to

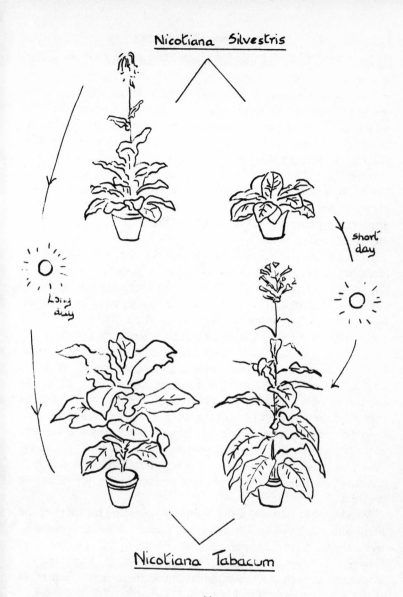

FIG. 44.
Interaction of environment and genotype in the flower formation of
tobacco plants. Nicotiana silvestris (top row) flowers only during the
long summer days of temperate zones. Nicotiana tabacum (bottom
row) flowers only during the short summer days of tropical countries.

be related. A geneticist who analyzed the data came to a conclusion which later was supported by large-scale family investigations in Indiana. It seems that a recessive gene (not sex-linked) allows the virus to invade the nerve cells, where it produces paralysis. The gene is not fully penetrant, and about one quarter of those who are homozygous for it escape with a minor general illness or remain well. So do persons who are heterozygous for the gene or do not carry it at all. Thus virus, genotype, and external circumstances—like bodily exercise in the early stage of infection—interact to produce infantile paralysis. The situation is similar for other infectious diseases, in particular for tuberculosis. We shall hear more about this in the next chapter.

Cancer is such a frequent disease that the occurrence of several cases in the same family cannot be taken as evidence for heredity, the more so as relatives are likely to be exposed to the same circumstances known or suspected to produce cancer, for instance work in a uranium mine or excessive smoking. There is, in fact, not much ground for inferring a genetical tendency for cancer in general. On the other hand, there seems to be a genetical element in the tendency to develop a particular type of cancer. In mice, genetically uniform strains have been bred in which a high proportion of animals develops some specific type of tumor, for instance, of the breast or of the lung. In man, where even close relatives differ widely in genotype, relatives of cancer patients run only a slightly increased risk of developing the same type of cancer. This should not cause them undue worry, but it should make them attentive to symptoms that might be a prelude to the type of cancer prevalent in their family.

What applies to traits of the body is equally true for those of the mind and the emotions. Intelligence, special abilities, personality traits are all due to an interaction of genetical and environmental factors. To assess the relative contributions of genotype and environment to such traits is a difficult task. In the next chapter we shall discuss one way of tackling it.

But first let us pause for a moment and look back to the quotation at the beginning of this chapter. Our discussion has led us far away from the notion that our genes—like the astrologer's stars—determine our constitution, personality, and through these, much of our fate. Rather we should look upon our genes as the cardplayer looks upon the cards that have been dealt out to him and with which he will have to do the best he can.

This comparison is, indeed, true in more than one sense. We shall see in Chapter 19 that, as the cards are shuffled before distribution, so are the genes of the parents shuffled before they are handed on to the children. Moreover, as the value of any particular card may be enhanced or diminished by the rest of the

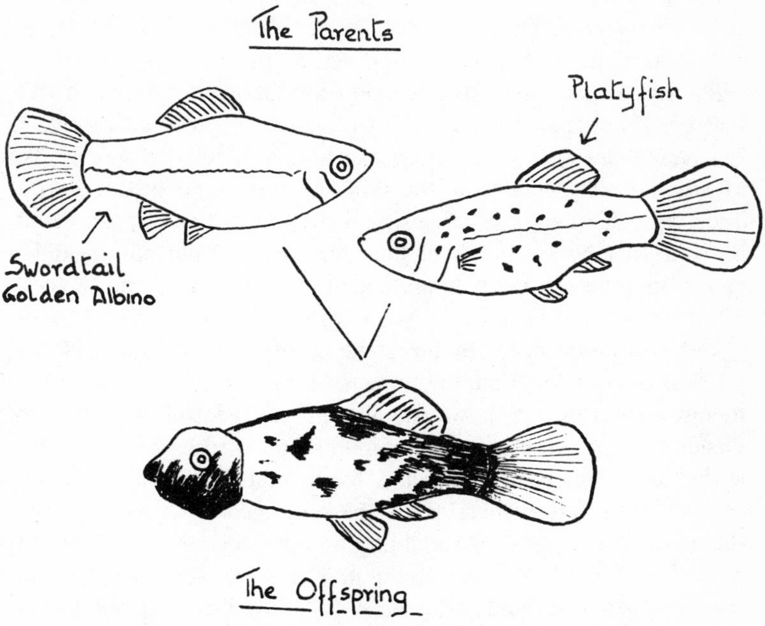

FIG. 45.
Influence of the genes on each other's effects. A swordtail (left) is mated with a black-spotted platyfish (right). The hybrid (below) has developed black tumors.

cards in the same hand, so may the value of a particular gene depend on the other genes in the same individual. If you have two X chromosomes, the gene that increases the uric acid content of the blood will rarely do you harm; if you have an X and a Y, it may give you painful attacks of gout. The aesthetically pleasing combination of genes for blue eyes and black hair is valueless for persons who at the same time are homozygous for the albino gene, which suppresses the formation of any kind of color in hair and eyes. Occasionally, an unusual combination of genes may produce a striking abnormality. Some varieties of the little Platyfish have attractive black spots; when these fish are crossed with the remotely related swordtail, the hybrids often develop nasty black tumors (Fig. 45). Here genes that in their original setting are harmless and, possibly, useful become dangerous in combination with an alien set of genes. Let me hurry to add that these crosses between different genera of fish are in no way comparable to crosses between human races.

We start life with a hand of genes as the cardplayer starts a game with a hand of cards. Occasionally, the hand may be so bad that even moderate success is out of reach. Even more rarely, it is so excellent that little or no exertion is required for success. Mostly, success depends on the skill and experience of the player. True enough, the limits of his achievement are set by the hand he holds and by the hands of the other players; but how near he comes to reaching these limits depends on his skill, and a good player may achieve a better score with poor cards than a poor player with good ones. In the game of life, the "playing" of the genes is only in part done by human efforts; the rest has to be left to circumstances which we cannot, as yet, control. Progress in this direction is, however, rapid. Smooth hair can be "permanently" curled, dark hair can be bleached. More important: speech defects caused by hereditary harelip can be prevented by operation, and the gene that causes susceptibility to infantile paralysis can be made harmless by polio vaccination. The more we find out about the ways genes act and the manner in which they respond to environmental conditions the more we shall learn to bring out the effects of the good genes and mitigate those of the bad ones.

CHAPTER 17 *Twins*

How IS IT possible to disentangle the effects of heredity from those of environment, since every living organism is the result of both? The general problem is familiar to scientists, and they have developed a standard method for dealing with it. Consider, for instance, one of the fundamental laws of electrical science. The amount of current that flows though an apparatus depends both on the voltage applied and on the resistance of the apparatus. There can be no current without voltage, nor can there be an apparatus without resistance. Nevertheless, physicists have managed to study the effects of each of these factors as it were in isolation. The effect of voltage was studied by recording the current when different voltages were applied to one and the same apparatus. The effect of resistance was studied by recording the current that one and the same voltage produced in apparatus of different resistance. Applied to the problem of heredity and environment, this method demands two complementary approaches. In the first, the effect of heredity is studied by observing how organisms of different genotypes develop in the same environment. In the second, the effect of environment is studied by observing how genetically identical organisms develop in different environments.

Both methods can be applied readily to organisms like bacteria or yeast which, by repeated divisions, grow into clones of genetically identical cells (Chap. 5). In many higher plants, clones arise through asexual propagation by cuttings, bulbs, tubers or the like. Thus, all "Golden Wonder" potatoes grow into genetically identical plants, and differences between these plants are due to environmental causes. Conversely, "Golden Wonder" and "Red Soil" are genetically different, and if they are grown together under as nearly as possible identical conditions, differences between the plants are mainly due to differences in genotype.

In higher animals and man, control of the environment is difficult, and complete control is impossible. All the same, individual components of environment, such as food and temperature, can often be compared with a fair amount of accuracy. A much more difficult problem is how to obtain a clone of genetically identical animals or humans. Reproduction in higher animals is always sexual and results in segregation for genes for which the parents are heterozygous. Since every human being is heterozygous for a large number of genes, even brothers and sisters are far from identical in genotype. We shall discuss this more fully in Chapter 19. There are, however, two ways for obtaining clones of genetically identical animals or humans. One, to be dealt with in Chapter 22, consists of close and long-continued inbreeding; it is a difficult and laborious method and has so far been used successfully only for laboratory animals. The other way is followed by Nature and is called identical twinning. It has provided geneticists with a powerful tool for the study of the nature-nurture problem in man and, more recently, also in cattle.

Everybody knows that there are two different types of twins. Some twins resemble each other no more closely than ordinary brothers and sisters; often one is a boy, the other a girl. These twins are called "ordinary," or "fraternal," twins. They are produced when a woman happens to release two ova simultaneously and both are fertilized. This kind of twinning occurs exceptionally in our species, but is the rule in all animals that produce litters. Fraternal twins are littermates and are genetically no more alike than pups in a litter. The other type of twins are always of the same sex and resemble each other so closely that even their parents may have difficulty in knowing them apart (Plate V, I). It is said that bloodhounds, for which every human being has a recognizably characteristic smell, cannot distinguish between the odors of identical twins and, in the hunt for a criminal, may be led astray by the tracks of his twin brother. These twins are called "identical." They arise through a peculiarity of embryonic development which is the

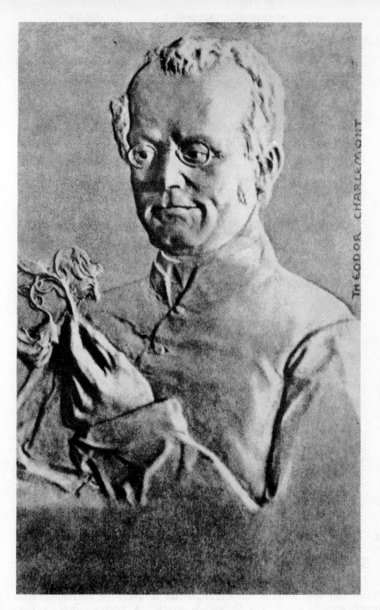

Plaque of Gregor Mendel.

PLATE I

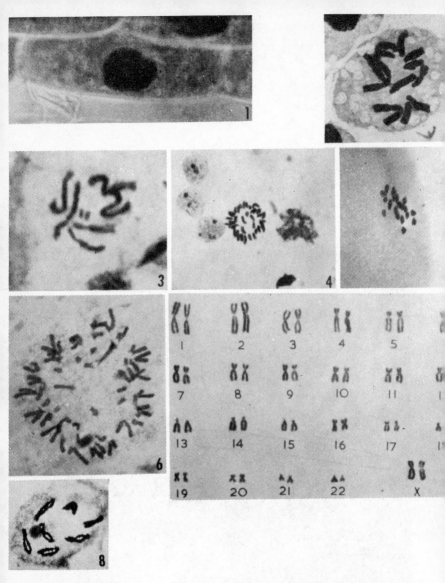

1. Plant cell with nucleus. 2. Chromosomes in a cell of the broad bean. 3. Chromosomes in a cell of a Drosophila female. 4. Chromosomes in a cell of a mouse female. 5. Chromosomes in a mouse ovum. 6. Chromosomes in a bone marrow cell of a woman. 7. Human chromosomes arranged in pairs. 8. Rye chromosomes in meiosis.

PLATE II

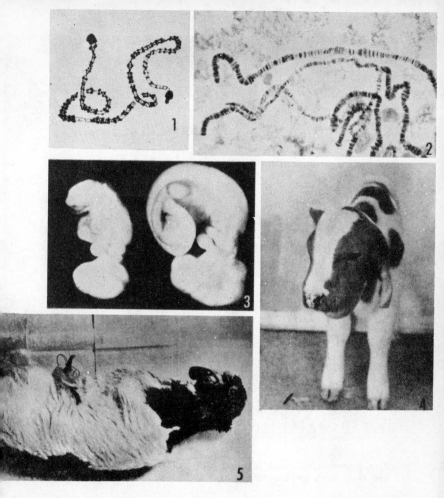

1. One pair of rye chromosomes at the beginning of meiosis. 2. Giant chromosomes in the salivary glands of Drosophila. 3. Embryos of tailless (left) and normal (right) mouse at the same age. 4. Dropsical calf. 5. Amputated calf.

PLATE III

Top, Ancobar fowl, dark hen and light cock. Below, Cambar chicks; the first and third from left are pullets.

PLATE IV

1. Identical twins, aged 95.

2. Dwarf mouse with normal littermate.

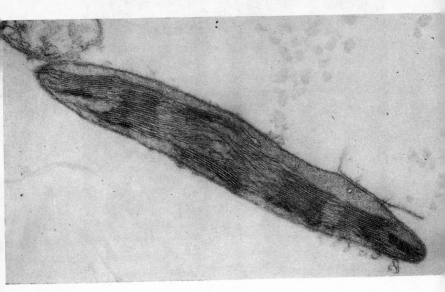

1. Chloroplast of barley, as seen through the electron microscope.

2. Tobacco leaves: left, normal; center and right, with mosaic virus disease.

PLATE VI

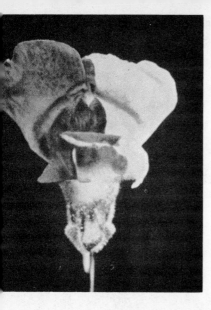

1. Mosaic snapdragon flower.

2. Recombination in a cross between two dog breeds—dachshund and Pekingese.

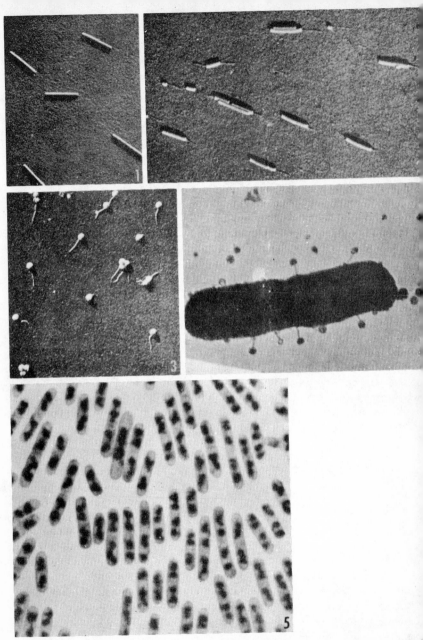

1. Particle of tobacco mosaic virus.   2. Tobacco mosaic virus, partially stripped of protein.   3. Bacteriophages.   4. Bacteriophages attacking bacterium.   5. Bacterium with nuclear bodies.   (Note: 1-4 are electron micrographs and are magnified from ten to fifteen times as much as 5, which was obtained through an ordinary light microscope at a magnification of several thousand times.)

PLATE VII

exception in man, but is the rule in a very different type of animal, the armadillo.

Toward the end of the nineteenth century a German naturalist heard from the natives of Brazil that a litter of armadillos always contains young of only one sex. The naturalist, with scientific skepticism, attributed this peculiar finding to the difficulty of sexing young armadillos correctly. The Brazilians, however, were proved right by later investigations, which also furnished the explanation of this curious phenomenon. When an armadillo female mates, only one ovum is fertilized. It grows into an embryo which, at a very early stage of development, divides into two. These, in turn, divide once more to give four embryos. In some species this process is repeated for a third time, so that eight embryos are formed. Thus the four or eight littermates are all derived from the same fertilized ovum and contain the same chromosomes and genes. Like cuttings from the same tree, they form a clone of genetically identical individuals. Since sex is determined by the chromosome constitution, they are of the same sex. Moreover, although to the human eye one armadillo looks very much like another, to the more discerning eyes of other armadillos littermates undoubtedly will appear strikingly similar (Fig. 46).

In man, identical twins arise by a similar process of early embryonic splitting. They are, as it were, the two halves of what originally was meant to be one individual. When splitting occurs so late that the embryo has already started to form a left-right pattern, the twins may be mirror images of each other in various traits. Thus, one twin may be right-handed, the other left-handed; or the hair on top of the head may have a clockwise whorl in one twin, an anticlockwise whorl in the other. Occasionally, there are further divisions of one or both twin embryos; these lead to identical triplets, quadruplets or quintuplets. More often, all or some members of these larger groups are fraternal twins.

In identical twins Nature provides material for studying the effects of environment on identical genotypes. In all characters that are strictly gene-determined, like sex, eye color, and blood group, identical twins are alike. They are also alike in the constitution of their proteins, so that skin grafting between identical twins can be carried out successfully (cf. Chap. 10). In characters which, like weight and intelligence, depend on environment as well as heredity,

Armadillo and Quadruplets

FIG. 46.
Identical quadruplets in the armadillo, and segregating pups in a litter.

identical twins usually differ more or less from each other. The average amount of this difference gives an indication of the relative importance of heredity and environment in determining the trait in question. Thus the observation that, on the average,* identical twins differ more in weight than in height is taken to mean that environment plays a relatively smaller role in determining stature than weight, and this is confirmed by other twin studies to be discussed presently. This conclusion may be expressed equally well by

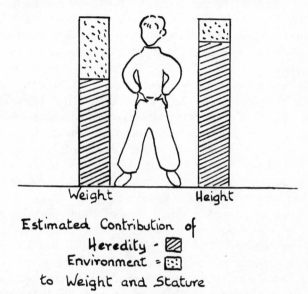

Estimated Contribution of
Heredity - 🔲
Environment = 🔲
to Weight and Stature

FIG. 47.
Effects of genotype and environment on weight and stature.

saying that heredity plays a relatively larger role in determining stature than weight; for, as heredity and environment between them shape the phenotype, a smaller contribution by one of them means a correspondingly larger contribution by the other (Fig. 47).

IDENTICAL GENOTYPES IN DIFFERENT ENVIRONMENTS

From the geneticist's point of view it is unfortunate that normally the environment of twins is very similar, much more similar than that of ordinary brothers and sisters who, although also growing

* For an explanation of the exact meaning of "average" see Chapter 21.

up in the same family, do so at different times. Comparisons between identical twins who have grown up in their own family will therefore tend to underestimate the force of environment. Widely divergent environments might well produce much larger differences between identical genotypes. That this is, in fact, the case was shown by a study of identical twins who, from an early age on, had grown up in different surroundings.

Twenty such cases were collected between 1923 and 1934, half of them through the offer of a free trip to the Chicago Fair, where some twin pairs of opposite sex became friendly with each other and created surprise and sensation by sauntering through the crowd as exactly duplicate couples. Many of these twins had interesting life histories to tell. Several of them had been fostered out so early that they did not even know of each other's existence until some dramatic encounter made them aware of it. Thus when Edith, working as a clerk in her foster father's store, was accosted familiarly as "Fay" by a strange young salesman, she at first rebuffed him suspiciously; but finally his insistence led to Edith's discovery of her twin sister. Helen, a schoolteacher, was put on the track of her twin sister when one of her favorite pupils complained that Helen had not greeted her at a concert.

The study of separately reared identical twins provided much interesting information on the extent to which environment can modify inherited traits. In most physical measurements, such as stature and head length, the separately raised twins were as much alike as identical twins reared together. An exception was weight, which proved highly modifiable by environment. While the average weight difference between the members of 50 pairs of identicals reared together was 4.1 pounds, that between the members of 20 pairs reared apart was 9.9 pounds. Average differences in intelligence quotient, scholastic performance, and personality traits also were increased by separation, the more so the greater the difference between the social and cultural backgrounds of the two foster homes.

Obviously, however, this type of approach to the nature-nurture problem in man is limited by the fact that the scientist has to take his cases where he finds them and cannot control the environments in which the separated twins are brought up. A rabid geneticist may wish for the chance of separating identical quadruplets at birth

and having them reared in a Fifth Avenue apartment, an Indian
wigwam, a Moscow orphanage, and an Eskimo igloo, respectively;
our society, fortunately, will not allow him to carry out such an
experiment. A more modest method for studying the effects of
controlled environmental conditions on identical twins was used
between the two world wars at the Maxim Gorki Institute in Moscow and has given interesting results. Over a thousand twin pairs,
most of them children, were investigated. Much of the work was

FIG. 48.
The effect of training on identical twins.

concerned with the effects of early training. Thus in one experiment
several pairs of identical twins of preschool age were trained in
making constructions with building blocks. All were given the same
blocks and had to build the same structures; but while one member
of each pair worked from a picture in which the position of each
block was indicated, the other member had to copy a model in
which the individual blocks were covered by paper (Fig. 48). After
two months of this training a clear difference in building skill had
developed within each pair. Without exception, the twin trained by

the second, more difficult method not only did better in working by either method but also in free creative construction. This type of twin research would appear to hold out much promise for studies of the environmental factors that influence the physical and mental development of children.

A similar method has been used for investigating the effect of different types of nutrition on the development of calves. Cattle twins, like human twins, are of two kinds: identical and fraternal. As in humans, identical twins are recognized by their striking similarity in all traits that depend mainly or only on heredity, such as sex, presence or absence of horns, coat color and pattern, and nose prints. Curiously enough, blood groups cannot be used for classifying cattle twins; for the fusion of blood vessels in fraternal twins, which in pairs of opposite sex produces a freemartin (Chap. 14), results in a mixture of the blood-forming cells, so that each fraternal twin shows not only his own blood group but also that of the other twin. Like identical human twins, identical calf twins are as a rule very much attached to each other. When a number of twin pairs stand in a byre, each calf regulates its behavior by that of its twin and not by that of its neighbor on the other side. When a twin herd is let out on pasture, twin calves stay close together, play with each other, and feed and rest at the same time. The kind of information that can be gained in experiments on identical cattle twins is illustrated in Fig. 49. It shows two pairs of identical twin heifers at two years of age. One twin of each pair had been reared on more and better food than the other; as a result this twin grew more quickly than its partner. At the time shown in the illustration, the well-fed Sara 214 weighed almost 500 kilograms, while her poorly fed twin sister Sara 213 weighed less than 350 kilograms; similarly the well-fed Spetsa 208 weighed slightly more than 350 kilograms, while her poorly fed twin sister Spetsa 207 weighed less than 300 kilograms. The differences between Sara 214 and Sara 213 and between Spetsa 208 and Spetsa 207 are entirely due to the different diets on which they had been raised. However, on both kinds of diet the Saras did better than the Spetsas; in fact, the poorly fed Sara 213 weighed almost as much as the well-fed Spetsa 208. The difference between the pairs of twins is due to their different heredity. Since the genetically superior animal on the poor diet grew almost as well as the genetically inferior one on the rich

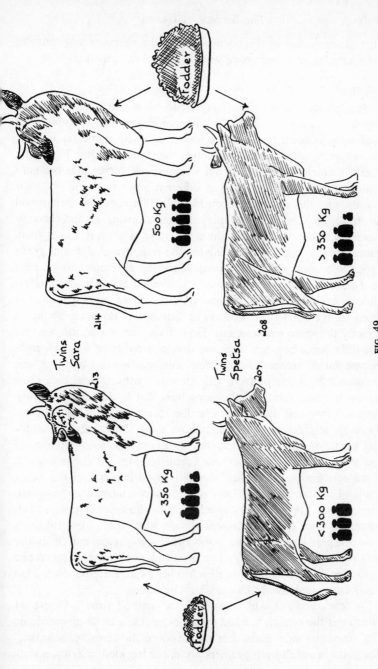

FIG. 49.
Effect of nutrition on growth in identical twin calves.

diet, it seems that in this particular case the effects of environment and heredity in determining weight were about equal.

DIFFERENT GENOTYPES IN SIMILAR ENVIRONMENT

Everybody knows from experience how strikingly different brothers and sisters may be in appearance as well as in intelligence and temperament. If they have grown up in the same family, one is inclined to attribute this variability mainly to heredity. No doubt, there is much truth in this; but we must not forget that ordinary brothers and sisters grow up at different times in the life of their family, and this may mean considerable differences in background at home, in school and at play. Fraternal twins are brothers or sisters who happen to grow up at the same time; this makes them more suitable material for studying the response of different genotypes to a common environment. Since the environments of boys and girls differ more than those of like-sexed children, it is preferable to exclude unlike-sexed pairs from such an investigation. Yet even so, fraternal twin brothers or twin sisters do not grow up in exactly the same environment. How, then, can we decide whether the differences between them are due to heredity or to small environmental differences? Fortunately, this question can be fairly well answered by a comparison with identical twins. These, too, grow up in the same family at the same time, but in this case we know that *all* observed differences are due to environment. If fraternal twins show differences over and above those found between identical twins, we may conclude that these are due to differences in genotype. Comparisons between identical twins on the one hand, fraternal twins on the other have developed into one of the major tools of human genetics. They may be supplemented by comparisons between the members of other pairs whose genotypes or environments have different degrees of similarity. Thus, identical twins reared apart have the same genotype, but more or less dissimilar environments. Genetically, brothers and sisters, or parents and children, differ as much from each other as do fraternal twins, but their environments are less similar (Fig. 50).

A few examples will show how the method works. Figure 51 illustrates the occurrence and extent of *freckling* in 87 identical and 107 fraternal twin pairs. Let us introduce the term "concordant" for pairs in which both partners are either freckled or not freckled,

	Heredity	Environment	
Identical Twins (reared apart) I	Identical	Different	
Identical Twins (reared together) II	Identical	Similar	
Fraternal Twins (reared together) III	Different	Similar	
Brothers or Sisters IV	Different to the same degree as in III	Less similar than in III	
Parent and Child V	Different to same degree as in III	Less similar than in IV	

FIG. 50.
Degrees of difference in heredity and environment between relatives.

FIG. 51.
Freckling in twins.

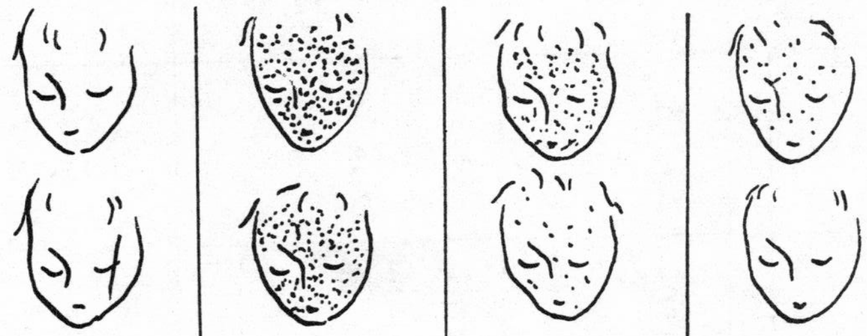

	Concordant		Discordant		Concordant	Discordant
Identicals	17	54	16	0	87	0
Fraternals	41	10	21	29	78	29

and the term "discordant" for pairs in which one partner is freckled, the other not. We shall then find that all 87 identical pairs are concordant, while among the 107 fraternal pairs 29 are discordant. This suggests that the presence or absence of freckling is a question of genotype, and that in the discordant fraternal pairs one twin has the gene or genes for freckling, the other has not. This conclusion has been borne out by other studies, and freckling is used as one of the traits by which identical and fraternal twin pairs can be distinguished. Twins who are discordant in regard to freckling are considered not to be identical. The converse is, of course, not true for, as Fig. 51 shows, concordant pairs may be either identical or fraternal.

While the presence of freckling is wholly gene-determined, its extent is not; for among the 70 identical pairs with freckles, there are 16 in which one member is heavily freckled, the other lightly. Presumably, the twins in these pairs had been exposed to very different amounts of sunlight. Among the 37 fraternal pairs with freckles, no less than 27 differed markedly in degree of freckling, and this is probably due to differences of genotype as well as of environment.

When a character depends on environment as well as on heredity, identical twins will not always be concordant in regard to it. Ordinary *rickets,* belong in this class of characters. Figure 52 shows the results of a twin investigation on rickets. Only pairs in which at least one member was affected were used in this study so that concordance for absence of rickets has not been recorded. Discordance, that is, rickets in one twin but not in the other, occurred 58 times among 74 pairs of fraternals, but only 7 times among 60 pairs of identicals. Three conclusions can be drawn from these data: (1) The fact that the majority of fraternal twins are discordant shows that, at least among the families studied, a common environmental deficiency was not usually sufficient to produce rickets. (2) The fact that, in contrast to fraternal twins, most identical twins were concordant shows that hereditary disposition plays a strong role in the causation of rickets. (3) The fact that 7 out of 60 pairs of identical twins were discordant shows that hereditary disposition alone does not produce rickets, and that the occurrence of rickets in a genetically disposed child can be prevented. This was well illustrated by two cases of discordance between identical twins where it turned out that the healthy child had been in a hospital for some unrelated illness and there had been given preventive treatment with vitamins.

About the year 1940 a large-scale investigation into the hereditary disposition for *tuberculosis* was carried out in the United States. Over a period of five years all resident or newly admitted tuberculosis patients in all hospitals and tuberculosis clinics of New

	Both affected	One affected
Identical Twins	53	7
Fraternal Twins	16	58

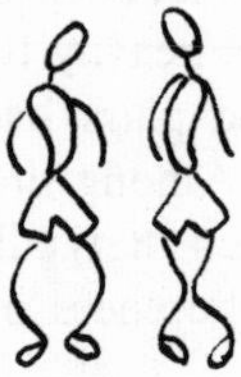

FIG. 52.
Rickets in twins.

York State and City were asked whether they had a twin brother or sister. Those who had (334) were used as the so-called "index cases," and their families (over 2,000 persons) were examined for further cases of tuberculosis. Some of the results are shown in Fig. 53. While the incidence of tuberculosis in the general population of the district was between 1 and 2 per cent, it was much higher among all relatives of the index cases. Thus, among 930 brothers and sisters of the index cases, 25.5 per cent also suffered from tuberculosis. In terms of concordance and discordance, 25.5

per cent of the brothers and sisters were concordant with their particular index case, while 74.5 per cent were discordant with it. In part, concordance for tuberculosis among relatives must be attributed to infection and similarity of environmental conditions, such as poor housing or malnutrition. The effects of environmental conditions are seen from a comparison between the incidence of tuberculosis in the parents and the sibs (brothers and sisters) of the index cases. Genetically, parents and children are as closely related

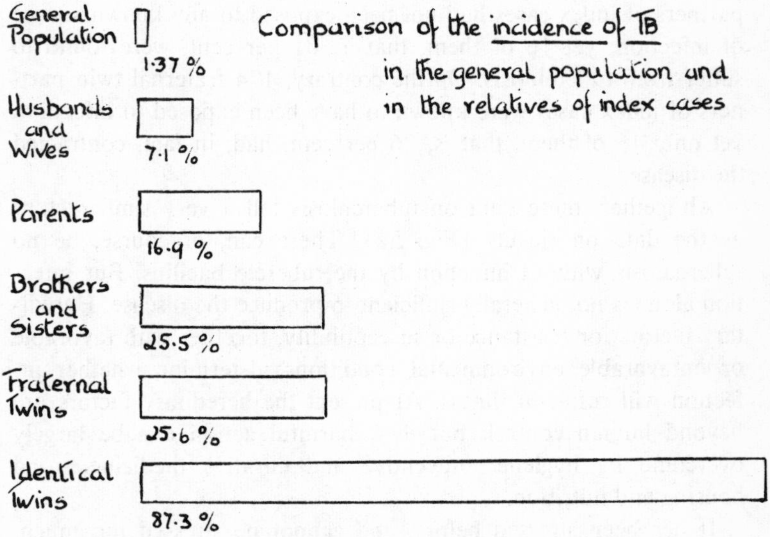

FIG. 53.
The interaction of heredity and environment in the
causation of tuberculosis.

as brothers and sisters; but the environment is more similar for children growing up in the same household than for children and their parents. Accordingly, the incidence of disease was lower among the fathers and mothers than among the brothers and sisters of the index cases. Yet differences in environmental similarity, including opportunity for infection, cannot explain the whole of the data; in particular they cannot account for the steep increase in disease frequency from the fraternal to the identical twins of the index cases. It is true that environmental similarities are somewhat greater for identical than for fraternal twins when both grow up in their own family; for an individual helps shape his own environment, and the very fact that identical twins have the same genes will make them inclined to choose the same occupations and companions. Nevertheless, this can account for only a small portion of the differences between fraternal and identical twins in degree of concordance for tuberculosis. The remainder must be attributed to genes for susceptibility to tuberculosis, which are always shared by identical twins but only occasionally by fraternal ones. Other observations point in the same direction. Thus, 26 identical twin partners of index cases had not been exposed to any known source of infection; yet 16 of them, that is, 61 per cent, were found to suffer from tuberculosis. On the contrary, 174 fraternal twin partners of index cases were known to have been exposed to infection; yet only 46 of them, that is, 26 per cent, had, in fact, contracted the disease.

Altogether, these data on tuberculosis tell a very similar story as the data on rickets (Fig. 52). There can, of course, be no tuberculosis without infection by the tubercle bacillus. But infection alone is not generally sufficient to produce the disease. Hereditary factors for resistance or susceptibility, together with favorable or unfavorable environmental conditions, determine whether infection will result in illness. At present the hereditary factors are beyond human control; but their harmful action can be largely overcome by hygiene, preventive and curative medicine, good housing and nutrition.

It has been stressed before, and cannot be stressed too much, that heredity is not a doom. Once we know how to prevent and cure a disease, we can prevent and cure it whether it is hereditary or not. In particular does this apply to the many diseases that are caused by a harmful outside agency acting on a hereditarily susceptible constitution. *Mental disease,* like physical disease, often has a genetical component; there are genes that produce in their carriers a tendency to break down mentally under conditions of stress which can be overcome by genetically more favorably endowed individuals. This knowledge does not in the least detract from our hope for future progress in the prevention and cure of mental illness.

As a final example of the twin method, let us look at some data which illustrate the interplay of heredity and environment in producing *criminality*. Between the two world wars, a number of investigators in Germany, Holland and the United States collected twin index cases in prisons much as other investigators had collected twin index cases in hospitals. They then tried to find the twin

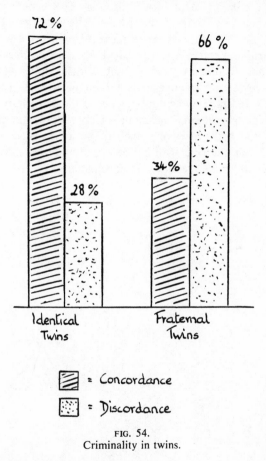

FIG. 54.
Criminality in twins.

brother or sister of the prisoner. If he (or she), too, had a criminal record, the pair was called "concordant"; if not, it was recorded as "discordant." In all investigations, identical twins were more often concordant than discordant; in all but one, fraternal twins were more often discordant than concordant. In addition, identical twins tended to commit the same type of crime, whereas fraternal twins often had been sentenced for quite different offenses. Fig. 54 shows the pooled data. Concordance is more than twice as high among identical twins than among fraternal ones, and although the greater intimacy between identical twins may contribute to this result, it can hardly explain it altogether. This conclusion is supported when one looks at the detailed life histories of the concordant pairs; for in many cases identical twins took to the same type of criminal career after they had led separate lives for many years. Thus criminality, like mental disease, appears to be the result of unfavorable environmental circumstances acting on a genetically receptive constitution. Again, the hereditary tendency to crime is not a doom. The more society succeeds in eliminating the environmental causes of crime, by improving social conditions and education, the rarer will be the opportunity for these undesirable genes to become manifest in criminal acts.

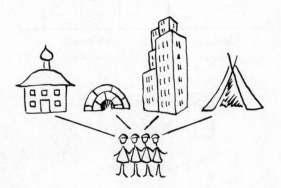

CHAPTER **18** *Is Intelligence Declining?*

=====

AFTER THE SECOND WORLD WAR the British government appointed a royal commission to study various features of the population. High among these studies ranked investigations on intelligence, and these led to a curious result and an alarming conclusion.

THE RESULT

In several investigations—some of them very extensive—children of the same age (usually 11 years) were given the same standard intelligence test, and their intelligence quotients (IQ) were calculated from these scores. When the data were grouped according to the number of children in the family, it was found that, *on the average,* the IQ was the lower the larger the family. The term "on the average" is crucial to this statement. It would be entirely wrong to conclude that every child from a large family was less intelligent than every child from a small one. Brilliant as well as stupid children were found in all groups, and many children from large families had higher IQ's than many from small families. Yet when the individual differences within each group were leveled out by, as it were, pooling all the available intelligence of the group and then dealing it out equally among all members, this "average group intelligence" increased with decreasing family size.

149

THE CONCLUSION

If, runs the argument, intelligent persons have fewer children than stupid ones because they marry later or plan their families more carefully, and *if* intelligence is at least partly determined by genes, then the children in large families will have inherited fewer genes for good intelligence than the children in small ones, and this will—at least in part—account for their lower average intelligence. Obviously, children from large families—simply because there are more of them—must contribute more grownups to the next generation than children from small families. The next generation will therefore contain not only a lower proportion of highly intelligent persons than the present one; it will also—as a whole—possess fewer genes for intelligence. If in this generation, too, the poor genes of the less intelligent persons are transmitted to more children than the good genes of the more intelligent ones, the generation after this will, on the average, be still less intelligent. And so the process will go on, human intelligence declining from generation to generation.

This was, indeed, a most disquieting prospect. On the basis of certain assumptions about the hereditary component in intelligence, predictions were made about the rate of decline, and finally these predictions were put to the test.

TEST OF THE CONCLUSION

In 1947 a standard intelligence test was given to practically all Scottish school children (70,805) whose eleventh birthday fell in that year. Exactly 15 years earlier the same test had been given to 87,498 Scottish school children of the same age. The interval between the two tests was half a generation, and the predicted decline in average intelligence should have been quite noticeable. Instead, there was a clear *increase,* although also in this investigation, as in all previous ones, the average IQ decreased with increasing family size.

RESOLUTION OF THE CONTRADICTION

Where, then, was the flaw in the argument, which seemed so reasonable and compelling? The whole argument would, of course, fall down at once if intelligence were quite independent of hereditary constitution, but this is not true. In fact, there is a fairly strong component in intelligence. This was shown in twin studies of the kind discussed in the preceding chapter. On the standard Binet scale, the average differences in IQ between fraternal twins was 9.9 points, while that between identical twins was only 5.9 points. Even though it is true that environmental differences within the home are somewhat smaller for identical twins than for fraternal ones (see p. 145), this alone cannot account for such a wide divergence between the two types of twins. Most of this divergence must be attributed to the fact that identical twins have all their genes in common, fraternal ones only some. Here, then, we see the influence of heredity on intelligence. We see it also from studies on the intelligence of foster children and their true and foster parents. On the average, the intelligence of these children was more similar to that of their true parents than of their foster parents, and this showed the effect of heredity. Yet there was also a strong similarity to the foster parents, and this must be attributed to the environmental influence of the foster home. Much clearer evidence for the existence of an environmental component in intelligence came from the study of identical twins reared apart. In a few cases, where the foster homes diverged widely in cultural background and provision of educational facilities, these twins differed strikingly in IQ, although it was not always the twin with the better educational opportunities who made the higher score. On the average, the difference in IQ within 50 such pairs was 8.2 points, that is, almost as great as between fraternal twins reared together. It seems that in this particular investigation the hereditary and environmental components of intelligence were about equally strong; larger environmental differences between identical twins might have shifted the balance in favor of the environmental component. In any case, there can be no doubt that intelligence is in large part gene-determined, and this brings us back to our argument.

Intelligence, as we saw just now, develops through the interplay of heredity and environment. The tests carried out in 1947 make it unlikely that the curious relationship between family size and average IQ of the children is caused by hereditary differences. Could it, instead, be due to environmental differences? This is, indeed, very plausible. It is evident that, in general, parents of small families can spend more money, time and attention on the individual child than parents of large families can. Moreover, at the time of these investigations there was a close connection between the professional status of a man and the size of his family. The higher the professional status the smaller—on the average—was the number of his children, so that children from small families tended to come from homes with a higher cultural background and, therefore, with a more favorable environment for the development of their innate mental capacities. Thus, for various reasons, large and small families provided different environments for the children. These differences were probably quite as large as those causing marked divergence of IQ in identical twins reared apart, and they would appear wholly sufficient to account for the observed decrease of average IQ with increasing family size. If this is true, the ghost of a mentally declining mankind is laid. Although it remains true that children from large families will form the majority of the next adult generation, most of them will by that time have outgrown whatever initial handicap to the full development of their inborn abilities had been imposed upon them by environment.

Some psychologists are still suspicious of this optimistic solution. They reason that the increase in IQ over the past 15 years is due to greater familiarity of modern children with intelligence tests, and that it may hide an actual decrease in innate intelligence. While the premise of this argument is probably correct (and, incidentally, is an admission of the strong environmental component in intelligence as measured by IQ), its conclusion is no more than an expression of personal misgivings and need not cause alarm, unless future observations should compel us to re-examine the whole question.

Similar misgivings have been raised by an observation that has already been mentioned. Investigations in various countries have consistently shown that, as one goes down the social scale, family size increases and average IQ of the children decreases. It is true that differences between individual children within the same class are very large, much larger than the average differences between the classes. The whole range of intelligence, from very brilliant to subnormal, is found in every class. Yet, when the class averages are calculated there is a definite decline from the highest to the lowest social level. In a recent British investigation, for instance, the average IQ of children decreased steadily from 120.3 in the higher professional class to 92.0 among unskilled workers. Doubtless, environmental influences must be largely responsible for this trend. Whether, in addition, inherited differences in intelligence play a role is a much and heatedly discussed question. On the whole, it seems likely that it should be answered in the affirmative, for it seems probable that, for example, university teachers as a class contain more men of high intelligence than unskilled laborers as a class. To the extent to which this is true, differences in family size between occupational classes may shift the over-all intelligence level of the population. But to what extent it is true is a question to which we have, at present, no answer. The more we succeed in providing equal educational facilities for children of all classes the better shall we be equipped for finding an answer.

When two groups differ widely in social, economic or cultural background it is impossible to know whether and to what extent differences between them in IQ are due to heredity. This applies to comparisons between Negroes and Whites in the United States. Consistently, the Whites have superior scores in intelligence tests carried out in any one state; but in tests carried out in the army in 1917 the average score of the Negroes in eight northern states was the same as that of the Whites in five southern ones. Now, it is true that we have good reasons for expecting genetical differences between human races (see Chap. 29). It is, therefore, not impossible that the genes that enable a person to excel in intelligence tests devised by Whites are more frequent among American Whites than among American Negroes. Whether or not one considers this as probable is, at present, no more than a rationalization of an emotional attitude. No reasonable conclusion can be drawn as long as there is no equality of environment and opportunity between the two groups.

CHAPTER 19 *The Game of Life: Mendel's Second Law*

IMAGINE A CARD GAME played by three players, whom we may call the father, the mother, and the child. When the game starts, father and mother each have the same number of cards, the child has none. The game consists of the child's acquiring his hand of cards according to certain rules:

(1) The first rule states that a hand has to consist of paired cards: a pair of aces, a pair of kings, and so on. There is, however, no restriction as to the set to which any card belongs. Thus all four kings in the father's and mother's sets may be kings of spades; or the father may have two kings of spades, the mother two kings of hearts; or all four kings may belong to different sets, and so on.

(2) The second rule prescribes that the child acquires his hand by drawing at random one—and only one—card from each of the pairs in the father's and the mother's hand.

(3) The third rule says that this has to be done independently for each pair; if, for instance, the father has laid out his pairs side by side, and if the child has chosen the left card from the first pair, he is free to choose either the left or the right card from the next pair, and so on through the whole row of pairs.

Figure 55 illustrates the results of one such game for four pairs of cards. The hand that the child happens to have drawn in this particular game is only one out of many others that he might have drawn equally well. Thus, instead of drawing the ace of hearts

154

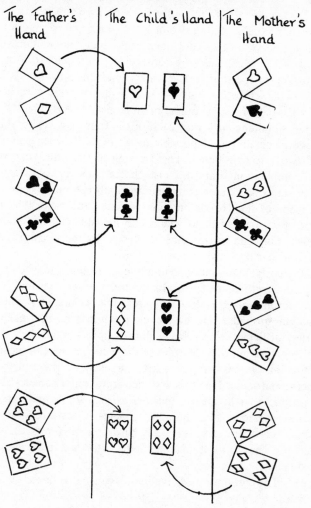

FIG. 55.
A card game played by father, mother and child.

from his father and the ace of spades from his mother, he might have drawn the other ace from either or both parents, that is, he might have acquired two aces of hearts, or one ace of hearts and one ace of diamonds, or one ace of spades and one ace of diamonds. Similarly, instead of acquiring two twos of clubs, he might have drawn a two of clubs together with a two of hearts, or a two of spades together with a two of hearts, or a two of spades together with a two of clubs. Altogether, this gives four combinations of twos, all of which had the same chance of being drawn. Since, according to the third rule of the game, the drawing of the twos had to take place without regard to the way the aces had been drawn, each of these four combinations of twos might have occurred simultaneously with each of the four possible combinations of aces. This makes 16 possible hands of cards when only the aces and twos are considered. The drawing of the threes can result in two combinations only, because the father's threes belong to the same set; since either combination of threes may occur together with any of the 16 combinations of aces and twos, this makes a total of 32 hands, all of which had an equal likelihood of being drawn. This number remains unaffected by the last draw, because the fours can be drawn in one way only.

Obviously, many more combinations are possible when the game is played with more cards. In nature, where the game is played with chromosomes instead of cards, this wealth of possible combinations provides one of the main sources of the inexhaustible variety of living beings. We shall now have to consider the way in which nature imposes the rules of the game on the chromosomes.

For this we have to go back to the early chapters of this book, where we discussed meiosis and the formation of gametes. You may remember that at meiosis partner chromosomes pair and subsequently segregate into different gametes. Considered for a single pair of chromosomes (Fig. 2), this process forms the basis of Mendel's first law. It also embodies the first two rules of our card game.

(1) The chromosomes, like the playing cards in our game, occur in pairs.

(2) At fertilization the child receives one—and only one—chromosome from each parental pair; which one is a matter of chance.

(3) The third rule comes into force when more chromosome pairs are considered.

We know that in each of the parents the chromosomes can be arranged into two sets, one—the paternal one—received through the spermatozoon, the other—the maternal one—through the ovum. From the child's point of view, each parent carries one grandpaternal and one grandmaternal set of chromosomes. The third rule of the game of chromosome transmission may then be expressed as follows: From each parent the child receives a random assortment of grandpaternal and grandmaternal chromosomes; if, for instance, among the chromosomes received from the father, Number 1 belongs to the grandpaternal set, Number 2 has an even chance of belonging to the grandpaternal or the grandmaternal set, and so on for all chromosomes received from either parent.

Figure 56 shows the mechanism by which this is achieved. It is a diagrammatic and much oversimplified representation of meiosis and gamete formation in a male with two pairs of chromosomes. One of the sets, let us say the paternal one, has been shaded in to distinguish it from the other. Shortly before segregation, the chromosome pairs come to lie side by side in the middle of the cell (I). Their position relative to each other at this stage determines the way in which they will subsequently be distributed into the gametes. For two chromosome pairs, two arrangements are possible, and both are equally probable. They have been shown in the diagram as II *a* and *b*. They lead to different sets of gametes (IV) each set consisting of two complementary combinations of chromosomes. Since both arrangements have the same chance of occurring, a sufficiently large sample of spermatozoa will contain all four possible combinations of chromosomes in equal frequencies. In the formation of ova the same processes occur, but only one out of each set of four gametes survives and develops into the ovum. However, since it is a matter of chance which particular gamete will survive, the final result will be the same as in the male: large numbers of ova will contain equal proportions of the four possible combinations of chromosomes. Lastly, since each of the four kinds of spermatozoa has an equal chance of fertilizing each of the four kinds of ova, the child has an even chance of receiving any one out of 16 possible combinations of two chromosome pairs, just as in the card game it had an even chance of receiving any one out of 16 possible combinations of two pairs of cards.

The genes must needs follow the movements of the chromosomes, and it was the way in which genes on different chromosomes combine in successive generations that led Mendel to the discovery of his second law, the "law of independent assortment" or "the law of free combination." Expressed in modern terminology, the law states that at gamete formation genes on different chromosome pairs segregate independently from each other and that all possible combinations between them will be found in the

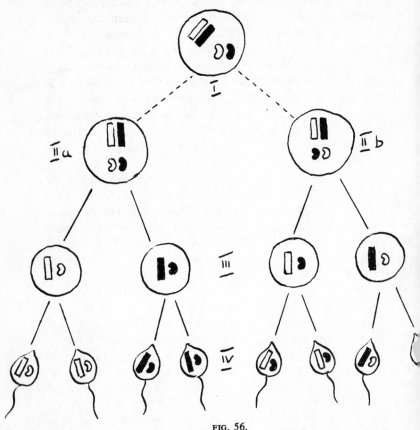

FIG. 56.
Meiosis for two pairs of chromosomes.

progeny. This law is equivalent to our third rule of the game, which states that the drawing of each pair of cards has to be done without regard to the way in which the other pairs have been drawn. Application of this rule makes it possible to work out the inheritance of several genes in the same pedigree. We shall illustrate this method by a few examples.

First, we shall look at one of the historical experiments with peas from which Mendel derived his second law. Instead of following him on his difficult road backwards from the result to the underlying law, we shall choose the easy road of showing that the law does, indeed, predict the result he obtained. In this particular experiment Mendel used strains of peas which differed in two pairs of characters instead of one, and he followed the way in which these characters combined in the progeny. One strain had round yellow peas, the other had wrinkled green ones. We know already that round seed shape is due to a gene *R,* which is dominant over its recessive allele *r* for wrinkled seed shape (Chap. 6). We also know what happens when a plant from the round-seeded strain is crossed with a plant from the wrinkled-seeded one (Fig. 11): the seeds of first-generation hybrids are all round; when they are grown into plants and these are self-fertilized, the second-generation seeds segregate into ¾ round and ¼ wrinkled ones. Similarly, Mendel found that yellow seed color is due to a gene *Y,* which is dominant over its recessive allele *y* for green seed color. In a cross between yellow-seeded and green-seeded plants the first-generation seeds are all yellow; when they are grown into plants and these are self-fertilized, the second-generation seeds segregate into ¾ yellow and ¼ green. These two pairs of genes are carried on different chromosome pairs, and Mendel's second law is therefore applicable to them. The essence of Mendel's second law is that the two segregations are completely independent of each other, as independent as successive draws in our game of cards. Suppose we sort the peas first into ¾ round and ¼ wrinkled. Then, according to Mendel's second law, segregation into color classes must be the same among the round as among the wrinkled peas. In the final result, the following classes will therefore be found among the second-generation peas:

¾ round $\begin{cases} \text{¾ of ¾} = \text{⁹⁄₁₆ are round and yellow} \\ \text{¼ of ¾} = \text{³⁄₁₆ are round and green} \end{cases}$

¼ wrinkled $\begin{cases} \text{¾ of ¼} = \text{³⁄₁₆ are wrinkled and yellow} \\ \text{¼ of ¼} = \text{¹⁄₁₆ are wrinkled and green.} \end{cases}$

This is exactly the result Mendel obtained, and it led him to the discovery of the law of independent assortment or free recombination. One particular noticeable point about this experiment is that four different types of peas were obtained in the second generation; in addition to the two original types, round yellow and wrinkled green, there were two new ones, round green and wrinkled yellow. Free recombination according to Mendel's second law is one of the main sources of genetic variability in nature and has formed the basis for many successful attempts by animal and plant breeders to combine in one strain advantageous characters of several.

The second example (Fig. 57) is taken from human inheritance. The simplified assumption has been made that the differences between brown and blue eyes and between curly and straight hair are due to single gene pairs, the gene for brown eyes (●) being dominant over the genes for blue eyes (○), and the gene for curly hair (ss) being dominant over the gene for straight hair (||). The father and the mother are both assumed to be heterozygous for the "curly" and "straight" genes and, therefore, are phenotypically curly-haired. The father has brown eyes, but is heterozygous for the "blue" gene. The mother has blue eyes and must be homozygous for the "blue" gene. In addition, the sex chromosomes of the father are X and Y, those of the mother are X and X. What are the chances that a child of theirs will be a boy or girl with any one of the four possible combinations of eye color and hair form: brown eyes and curly hair, brown eyes and straight hair, blue eyes and curly hair, blue eyes and straight hair?

In Fig. 57 the genes and sex chromosomes are represented as playing cards, and we shall find the answer to our question by applying the rules of our card game to the way in which the children of this particular couple may acquire their hands of cards. Let us start with the first pair, which carries the genes for curly or straight hair. There are four possible draws, but only one of them gives the child the two genes for straight hair that it requires in order to be phenotypically straight-haired. Any child of this marriage is therefore three times as likely to have curly hair as straight hair or, expressed differently, among all possible children of this couple there are three times as many with curly hair as with straight hair. The same could, of course, have been inferred from Mendel's first law applied to a cross between two heterozygotes (Chap. 6, Fig. 11).

We now come to the second draw, which decides whether the

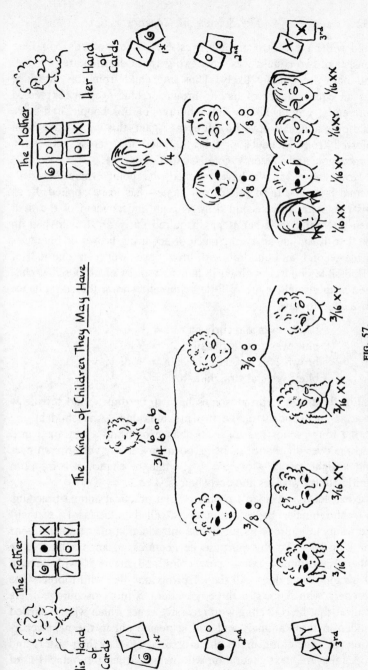

The Father

His Hand of Cards

6	1
0	•
X	Y

1st | 6 | 1 |
2nd | 0 | • |
3rd | Y | X |

The Kind of Children They May Have

3/4 6 or 6

3/8 ••

3/16 XX   3/16 XY

3/8 ••

3/16 XX   3/16 XY

The Mother

Her Hand of Cards

1st | 6 | 1 |
2nd | 0 | • |
3rd | X | X |

X	X
6	0
1	0

1/4

1/8 ••   1/8 ••

1/16 XX   1/16 XY   1/16 XY   1/16 XX

FIG. 57.

The game played with genes instead of playing cards.

child will have brown or blue eyes. Since the mother's pair here consists of two equal cards, only two ways of drawing are possible, and both are equally likely. Thus any child from this marriage has an equal chance of having brown or blue eyes or, expressed differently, among all possible children of this couple half have blue eyes and half have brown eyes. Again, this could have been inferred from Mendel's first law applied to a cross between a homozygote and a heterozygote (Chap. 6, Fig. 13).

Now, however, we have reached the point where Mendel's second law—the third rule of our game—has to be applied. If, as this rule states, the second draw is quite independent of the first, then any child, whether it has acquired curly or straight hair in the first draw, has an even chance of acquiring brown or blue eyes in the second, and children with brown eyes will form one half of all possible children with curly hair as well as of all possible children with straight hair. A little arithmetic shows that the chance for a child to have

$$\text{brown eyes and curly hair} = \tfrac{1}{2} \text{ of } \tfrac{3}{4} = \tfrac{3}{8}$$
$$\text{blue eyes and curly hair} = \tfrac{1}{2} \text{ of } \tfrac{3}{4} = \tfrac{3}{8}$$
$$\text{brown eyes and straight hair} = \tfrac{1}{2} \text{ of } \tfrac{1}{4} = \tfrac{1}{8}$$
$$\text{blue eyes and straight hair} = \tfrac{1}{2} \text{ of } \tfrac{1}{4} = \tfrac{1}{8}$$

Finally, the sex chromosomes have to be drawn, and this draw is again independent of the two previous ones. Any child in any of the four groups has an even chance of being a boy or a girl, and the over-all chance of being born, say, a boy with brown eyes and straight hair is $\tfrac{1}{2}$ of $\tfrac{1}{8} = \tfrac{1}{16}$, while the chance of being born a girl with brown eyes and curly hair is $\tfrac{1}{2}$ of $\tfrac{3}{8} = \tfrac{3}{16}$.

Next, let us consider a problem from practical animal breeding. A rabbit fancier has a strain of so-called "blue-fawn" animals. He wants to improve its fur by the introduction of the angora gene for long hair. To this purpose he acquires an angora buck with otherwise ordinary rabbit coat color and mates it with several of his blue-fawn does. All the offspring look like wild rabbits. The breeder, who knows a little genetics, is not discouraged. He realizes that he is dealing with recessive genes which will be carried hidden in these animals and will segregate out in the next generation. He, therefore, mates the crossbred ♂ ♂ to their sisters and hopes that the next generation will include at least 1 ♂ and 1 ♀ of the desired angora blue-fawn type, which he then can use as foundation animals for the new strain.

Unfortunately, the breeder's knowledge of genetics has been just sufficient to make him embark on an enterprise that is likely to lead to disappointment. Let us analyze his scheme by reference to a book on rabbit genetics. We find there that angora hair is due to a recessive gene *l*. Thus, the angora buck has the genotype *l l*. Next we look up the blue-fawn phenotype and find that it is due to the interaction of three recessive genes. One of these, *a*, abolishes the yellow banding of each hair that gives the wild-type coat its characteristic flecked appearance; animals homozygous for this gene alone are self-colored blacks. The second gene, *b*, changes the black pigment in the fur to brown, so that animals homozygous for both *b* and *a* have self-colored brown coats. The third gene, *e*, dilutes this brown coat color into a bluish fawn. The blue-fawn strain, therefore, is homozygous for all three genes. The book further tells us that the four genes *l, a, b* and *e* are all carried on different chromosomes, so that they combine in inheritance according to Mendel's second law. Now at last we have all the necessary tools for judging the rabbit breeder's scheme.

His original cross was between an angora ♂, genotypically *ll*, and blue-fawn ♀ ♀, genotypically *aa; bb; ee*. Neither strain carries the genes for which the other is homozygous, so that the progeny will be heterozygous for all four genes: *a+; b+; e+; l+*. These heterozygotes are crossed together:

$$a+; b+; e+; l+ \times a+; b+; e+; l+$$

The genotype in which the breeder is interested is *aa; bb; ee; ll*. What chance has he of obtaining it among the offspring of these matings?

As in the previous example, let us consider the genes one by one. The chance for any offspring to inherit one *a* gene from its father and a second *a* gene from its mother is ¼, according to Mendel's first law; the same is true for the other three genes. Thus, the chance for an animal to be

$$aa = ¼$$
$$bb = ¼$$
$$ee = ¼$$
$$ll = ¼$$

Since the genes are carried on different pairs of chromosomes, their combination occurs according to Mendel's second law, and the chance of obtaining animals that are *aa; bb; ee; ll* is ¼ of ¼ of ¼ of ¼ = 1/256. The chance of one of these animals being either a ♂ or a ♀ is half of this = 1/512, and since the breeder's scheme envisages obtaining both these animals in the progeny of the first crossbreds, he may well have to rear 600 or more young before he has achieved his end. He may, of course, be lucky and find a blue-fawn angora young already in the first litter; but he would need to be very lucky indeed to obtain both a ♂ and a ♀ of the right kind in a moderate-sized rabbitry.

A better knowledge of genetics would have made him plan differently. Among the progeny of the crossbreds he would pick any combinations in the right direction and either cross them together or to one of the original strains. If, for example, he found a black angora (genotype *aa; ll,* possibly heterozygous for *b* or *e* or both), he might cross this to animals from his blue-fawn strain, like this: *aa; (b+?); (e+?) ll × aa; bb; ee.* All the progeny of this cross will be black (*aa*) and heterozygous for *l, b* and *e;* some may even be homozygous for *b* or *e.* His task has therefore been reduced to the combination of 3 or 2 genes instead of 4. If, instead of a black angora, some other combinations of genes had turned up among the progeny of the first crossbreds, another breeding procedure might have been advisable.

I have dealt at some length with these two examples because they show how Mendel's second law can be used for predicting the frequencies with which combinations between paternal and maternal genes will appear in later generations. It is calculations like these much more than the famous textbook ratios of, for example, 9:3:3:1 (p. 159) or 27:9:9:9:3:3:3:1, that illustrate the consequences of the principle of "independent assortment."

Lastly, let us look at a practical breeding problem that cannot be solved by application of Mendel's second law. It concerns attempts to combine into one strain of mink two genes that are found separately in different strains: the dominant gene for ebony(*E*), and the recessive gene for brown-eyed pastel(*b*). These two genes are carried on the same chromosome pair, and when animals of the two strains are crossed, the offspring carries one gene on each of the two partners of this pair of chromosomes, like this

When such an animal forms gametes, the two chromosomes and with them the genes *E* and *b* segregate into different cells. Free recombination between these genes is not possible. It looks as though the only way to obtain a strain with both these genes consists in waiting until a mutation to ebony occurs in the brown-eyed pastel strain or a mutation to brown-eyed pastel in the ebony strain. This is likely to require not only many generations of minks, but also many generations of mink breeders. In actual fact, when heterozygotes for ebony and brown-eyed pastels were mated, some of the kits were "palomino," that is, ebony brown-eyed pastel. Their manner of origin will be described in the next chapter.

CHAPTER 20 *Linked Genes*

GENES THAT ARE carried on the same chromosome pair are called "linked." Linked genes do not obey Mendel's second law; they do not show free recombination with each other. In the mink the mutant genes for ebony and brown-eyed pastel are linked; so, of course, are their normal allelomorphs. Sex-linked genes are linked with the sex-determining genes on the X chromosome; necessarily, they are also linked with each other. In the following, two sex-linked genes will be used to illustrate the behavior of linked genes in inheritance.

In man, the mutant genes for red-green color blindness and hemophilia are sex-linked (Chap. 15) and, therefore, linked with each other. Occasionally, both mutant genes occur in the same family. Such families are of two different types.

Type I. In these families, the two mutant genes have been brought together through marriage between individuals carrying one or the other gene. The genes are thus carried on different X chromosomes; they are, in genetical terminology, linked "in repulsion" (Fig. 58, I, first row).

Type II. In these families, a mutation to one of these abnormalities, say hemophilia, occurred on a chromosome that already carried the other mutant gene. Both mutant genes are here carried on the same X chromosome; they are linked "in coupling" (Fig. 58, II, first row).

In either type of family, most women will be phenotypically normal; but many will be heterozygous for one or both mutant genes (Fig. 58, second row), and these women may have affected sons. Since a son inherits only one of his mother's X chromosomes, affected sons of Type I heterozygotes suffer from either hemophilia or color blindness, but not from both simultaneously (Fig.

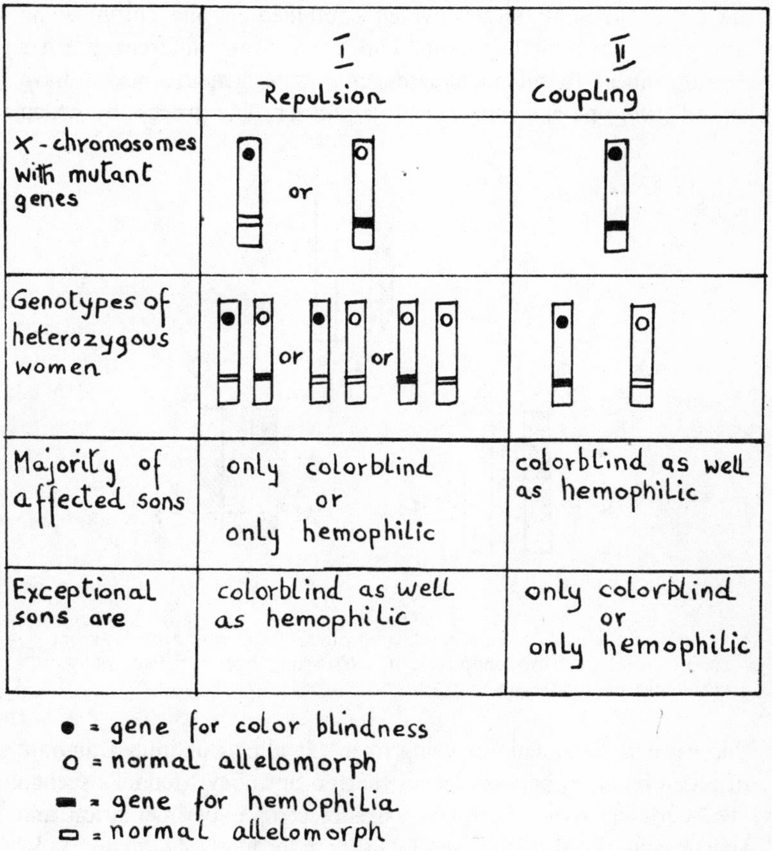

	I Repulsion	II Coupling
X-chromosomes with mutant genes	or	
Genotypes of heterozygous women	or or	
Majority of affected sons	only colorblind or only hemophilic	colorblind as well as hemophilic
Exceptional sons are	colorblind as well as hemophilic	only colorblind or only hemophilic

● = gene for color blindness
○ = normal allelomorph
▬ = gene for hemophilia
▢ = normal allelomorph

FIG. 58.
Linkage between the sex-linked genes for color blindness and hemophilia.

58, third row), while affected sons of Type II heterozygotes suffer from both disabilities. Exceptions, however, may occur. They are shown in the fourth row of Fig. 58. Very occasionally, a woman who carries the gene for color blindness on one X chromosome

and the gene for hemophilia on the other (Type I) may have a son
who shows both disabilities, or a woman who carries the gene
for both disabilities on the same X chromosome (Type II) may
have a son who suffers from only one of them.

It is easily seen that these exceptions are of the same kind as
the palomino mink kittens which combined in one chromosome
two genes that their parents had carried on different partner
chromosomes. In all such cases, a mutant gene seems to have
shifted from one chromosome to its partner. The process by which

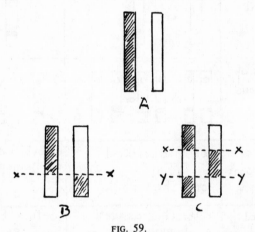

FIG. 59.

Crossing over. A. A pair of chromosomes. B. Crossing over at one
point: exchange of endpieces. C. Crossing over at two points:
exchange of middle pieces.

this happens is called "crossing over"; it allows a limited amount
of recombination between genes that do not obey Mendel's second
law. Crossing over has formed a subject of experimentation and
speculation for decades and is still not properly understood. Its
consequences, however, are well known indeed and, in any particular case, are as predictable as the consequences of Mendel's
laws. Figure 59 shows these consequences for the chromosomes
rather than for the genes carried on them. In the original chromosome pair (*A*) one partner has been shaded in to distinguish it
from the other. *B* and *C* are two of the many possible types of
crossing over that may take place in pair *A*. In both cases, there

has been an exchange of pieces between the partner chromosomes. In *B,* the exchange was between endpieces and required only one point of exchange (x); in *C,* the exchange was between middle pieces and required two points of exchange (x and y). The most important feature to note is the exact correspondence between the points of exchange in the partner chromosomes. Without such accuracy, partner chromosomes would soon cease to be equal in length; what is more, they would soon cease to be exactly matched in gene content, and chromosomes with too many or too few

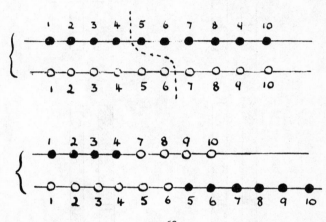

FIG. 60.

The necessity for accuracy in crossing over. If the points of exchange on the two chromosomes are not accurately matched (top row), the resulting chromosomes will lack genes (upper chromosome in bottom row) or carry genes in duplicate (lower chromosome in bottom row).

genes would be put into circulation and would result in abnormalities and death. If, for instance (Fig. 60), the exchange point in one of the chromosomes fell between the 4th and 5th gene and in the other between the 6th and the 7th gene, exchange between endpieces would give one chromosome that lacked genes 5 and 6 and a partner chromosome that had these genes in duplicate.

The most widely accepted view is that crossing over takes place at the beginning of meiosis when the partner chromosomes are not only paired closely and accurately but are also coiled round each other, so that the stress of twisting might cause them to break at identical points and join again with an exchange of partners. Other explanations have been sought, and at the moment no decision is possible.

By whatever mechanism this exchange of pieces between partner chromosomes is brought about, it can readily account for crossing

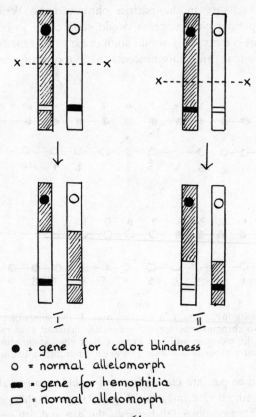

● = gene for color blindness
○ = normal allelomorph
▬ = gene for hemophilia
▭ = normal allelomorph

FIG. 61.
Crossing over between the genes for color blindness and hemophilia.

over as observed genetically. Figure 61 shows how it can explain the birth of a color-blind hemophilic son to a woman who carries the genes for these abnormalities on opposite chromosomes (I) or of a son with only one of these abnormalities to a woman who carries the genes for both on the same chromosome (II).

If chance decides where exchange points occur, one would

expect crossing over to take place more often between genes that are far apart along the chromosome than between genes that are close together, and this is indeed the case. When two genes are very close to each other, the chance that an exchange point will fall between them is low, and crossing over is rare. The greater the distance between two genes, the higher the chance of an exchange point falling between them, and the greater the frequency of crossing over. Beyond a certain distance from each other, two genes combine as freely as if they were carried on different chromosome pairs.

Historically and logically, this account puts the cart before the horse. It was the discovery of genetical linkage that made it possible to assign genes to chromosome pairs, and it was the discovery of crossing over that made it possible to measure distances between genes in terms of crossover frequencies. The statement that two genes are 10 crossover units apart is simply a shorter way of saying that a heterozygote for these two genes forms 10 per cent crossover gametes.

When a chromosome pair carries several or many known genes, crossing-over experiments can be used to construct a chromosome "map," which shows the order of the genes and their relative distances from each other. In Drosophila melanogaster, the genes for scarlet eyes (*st,* recessive), stubbly bristles (*Sb,* dominant), and curved wings (*cu,* recessive) are all carried on the third chromosome, one of the two long autosomes. The crossover distance between *st* and *Sb* is 14 per cent, that between *cu* and *Sb* is 8 per cent. These data alone are not sufficient for mapping the three genes, for they are compatible with two different arrangements (Fig. 62, I and II). When, however, it is found that the crossover distance between *st* and *cu* is 6 and that between *cu* and *Sb* is 8, the order *st cu Sb* is definitely established (Fig. 62, III). Other genes can be added to the map by the same method. At present the map of this particular chromosome shows the positions of over 150 genes. The fact that genes always *can* be mapped in this way is proof of their linear arrangement along the chromosomes. If the arrangement were otherwise, if, for instance, some genes were sticking out from the chromosome on side branches, the distances between three genes could not always be arranged in such a way that one is the sum of the other two (Fig. 63). Ac-

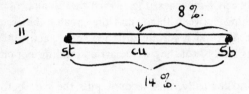

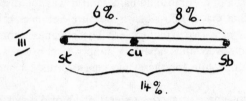

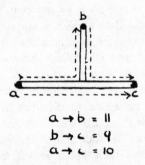

FIG. 62.
How genes are "mapped." Distance *st* to *Sb* = 14% crossing over; distance *Sb* to *cu* = 8% crossing over; distance *st* to *cu* = 6% crossing over. Therefore, the order of the genes is as shown in III.

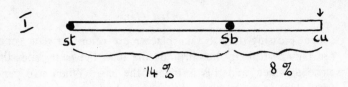

$$a \rightarrow b = 11$$
$$b \rightarrow c = 4$$
$$a \rightarrow c = 10$$

FIG. 63.
Proof that the chromosome has no side branches. If *b* lay at the end of a side branch, the distance from *a* to *c* would not be the sum of the distances from *a* to *b* and from *b* to *c*.

tually, it is usually slightly less than the sum; but this is a minor detail which can be explained and need not concern us here.

For the animal breeder the significance of crossing over lies in the opportunity it affords him of "recombining," that is, either combining or separating, linked genes. Whether or not this can be achieved easily and economically depends upon the distance between the genes in which he is interested. When the genes are far enough apart from each other, linkage is no obstacle to recombination. When they are sufficiently close for linkage to be noticeable, the breeder will have to calculate in advance whether his resources are adequate for the breeding program he has in mind. A mouse fancier who wants to cross a pink-eyed* strain with a chinchilla one in order to obtain pink-eyed chinchilla mice can achieve his object without too much cost and labor; for the crossover distance between the genes for pink eyes and chinchilla fur is about 15 per cent, so that heterozygotes which carry these genes in repulsion form about 15 per cent gametes that carry them in coupling. On the contrary, a mouse fancier who wants to isolate mice with "dilute" coat color and normal ears from a dilute short-eared strain had better consult a book on mouse genetics before deciding whether he will be able to complete his program; for the genes for dilute coat and short ears are very closely linked, and if a mouse carries both genes in coupling on one chromosome and both normal allelomorphs on the other, only 1 gamete among approximately 1,000 will carry the gene for dilute coat color without that for short ears.

---

* The pink-eye gene is different from the albino gene, which makes the fur white and the eyes pink and is, in fact, an allelomorph of the chinchilla gene (p. 65).

CHAPTER 21 *Johannsen's Beans*

A HUNDRED YEARS AGO Charles Darwin, in his famous book *Origin of Species,* wrote the following passage about the origin of domestic breeds of plants and animals: "We cannot suppose that all the breeds were suddenly produced as perfect and as useful as we now see them; indeed, in many cases, we know that this has not been their history. The key is man's power of accumulative selection: nature gives successive variations; man adds them up in certain directions useful to him." In Darwin's time, and for at least a century previously, breeders had consciously used selection of breeding stock as one of their main tools. Before that, as Darwin pointed out, much unconscious selection had resulted simply from the fact that a man would tend to keep his best animals for breeding and his best plants for seed collection. Yet selection is by no means always and equally effective. Darwin could not account for this except by reference to the "greater or less force of inheritance." With the rediscovery of Mendel's laws in 1900, this vague concept was filled with concrete meaning and could be used to explain and rationalize selection. The man who laid the ground for this was a Danish botanist, W. Johannsen.

In a series of experiments, which are known to every student of genetics, Johannsen tested the effects of selection on scarlet runner beans. Usually, the character for which he selected was size of beans. From among a sample of beans of various sizes he picked the largest and the smallest (Fig. 64, *a,b,*I) and grew them into plants (II). When these plants had produced beans, he harvested

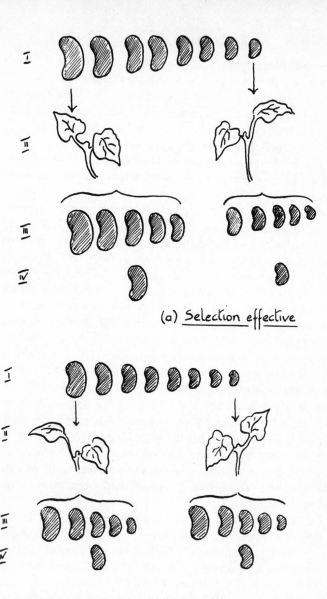

FIG. 64.
Selection for size in runner beans.

and measured them. It was not, of course, to be expected that all beans grown on the same plant would have the same size; but by measuring all of them Johannsen could determine their range of variation (III) and their average size (IV). The range of variation is simply the difference between the largest and the smallest bean. The term "average" requires some explanation. In ordinary life it is often used in the same sense as "normal" or "usual." In scientific language it has a more precise meaning, which may be illustrated by a homely example. Suppose a mother distributes a small basket of cherries among her four children by giving each of them a handful. When the children count their cherries, there is an outcry against the unfairness of the distribution, for, while Jim and Ann got 5 cherries each, Mary got 6 and Johnny as many as 8. To pacify the children, the mother gathers all cherries—24 altogether—and divides them into 4 equal lots of 6 each. Now each child has the average number, for 6 is the average of 5, 5, 6 and 8. In the same way, the average size of, say, 100 beans is calculated by adding together the total sizes of all the beans and dividing the sum by 100.

Let us now return to Johannsen's experiments. Figure 64*a* shows what happened when selection was effective; Figure 64*b* shows what happened when selection was ineffective. In the first case, the average size of the beans harvested from a plant depended on the size of the bean from which the plant itself had been grown: plants grown from large beans yielded beans of larger average size than plants grown from small beans. In the second case, the beans on all plants had the same average size and the same range of variation, independent of whether the plants had been grown from large or small beans.

When is selection effective and when is it ineffective? This was the important question that Johannsen set out to answer and did, in fact, answer once and for all. To formulate his answer, he invented two terms with which the reader is already familiar: genotype and phenotype. Selection, he showed, is effective only when the selected individuals differ genotypically from each other; phenotypical variation is not inherited and cannot, therefore, be preserved by selection. His material was very suitable for demonstrating this fundamental truth. Beans are naturally self-fertilizing, and continued self-fertilization gives individuals that are homozygous for all or almost all their genes. Why this is so, we shall see in the next chapter. For the moment, let us accept this fact and consider its consequences. If *A* and *a, B* and *b, C* and *c* are three pairs of genes, then a bean plant may have any one of the homozygous genotypes like *AA bb cc,* or *aa BB cc,* but none of the heterozygous ones like *AA Bb Cc.* When such a plant forms gametes, there is no segregation and all the gametes are alike; a plant of genotype *aa BB cc,* for instance, forms only gametes of genotype *a B c.* At self-fertilization, two like gametes fuse, and all the progeny will have the same genotype as the parent plant. The same applies to the rest of the genes. Thus all beans growing on the same plant have the same genotype. So have all the plants grown from these beans, and all the beans produced by them. This process can go on indefinitely until whole populations are formed the members of which are all alike genotypically. Johannsen called such populations "pure lines." Pure lines in sexually reproducing organisms are the equivalent of asexually produced clones, including identical twins. Like clones and twins, they can be used for determining the effects of environment on the same genotype. Variation between beans of the same pure line must be wholly due to environmental differences between plants, pods and locations within the same pod. When environment is highly uniform the differences between beans will be small; when environment is very variable they will be large. But no matter whether they are large or small, they are only phenotypical and are not inherited. Variation between beans of different pure lines is due to differences in genes as well as in environment; to the extent that it is due to genes it is heritable.

At this point we can return to Johanssen's experiments. What, we ask, was the difference between the experiments shown in Figs. 64*a* and 64*b*? The answer is now obvious. In *b,* the parent beans belonged to the same pure line; their differences were wholly phenotypical, and their progeny "reverted" (as one used to say in pre-Mendelian times) to the average of their line. In *a,* the parent beans were genotypically different; they belonged to different pure lines, and so did their progeny. Beyond this, no further selection was possible; for the remaining variation within each line was again wholly phenotypical.

Beans in a commercial sample will usually belong to many different pure lines. Each line has its range of variation, and these ranges overlap as in Fig. 64*a,* where beans 4 and 5 of the large line have the same sizes as beans 1 and 2 of the small one. "Mass selection," that is, selection of all beans above a certain size, will pick out not only genotypically large beans from the best pure lines in this regard but also phenotypically large beans from poorer lines. Eventually, this type of selection, too, will result in isolation of the best pure lines, but it will do this more slowly than the "individual selection" carried out by Johannsen. This type of individual selection is, however, restricted to self-fertilizing organisms. In cross-fertilizing species, that is, in all domestic animals and many domestic plants, selection is complicated by the inevitable segregation and recombination of genes in the selected parents. On the other hand, the continued reshuffling of genes presents selection with a constantly replenished source of new genotypical variation.

Johannsen's experiments demonstrate clearly the main problem of the breeder who wants to improve his stock by selection: how is he to distinguish between genotypical, inherited, and phenotypical, not-inherited, variation? The problem is made more difficult by the fact that most agriculturally important characters are quantitative in nature, that is, they do not refer to qualitative properties, like presence or absence of horns, black or white color, but to measurable differences such as egg yield per year or grain weight per acre. Such characters are easily influenced by environmental conditions, and even genotypically very similar individuals form whole arrays of intergrading phenotypes. Genetically, quantitative characters are determined by large numbers of genes with similar but individually small effects, and these, too, by forming many different combinations, produce arrays of intergrading phenotypes. It is often exceedingly difficult to decide whether a desirable phenotype is the result of good genes or good farm management; yet on the correct decision depends the success or failure of selection.

In agricultural research, the argument is sometimes reversed, and the extent to which selection is effective is taken as a measure of "heritability" of the selected character. In cattle, for instance, it is easier to select for high fat content of the milk than for high over-all milk yield, and selection for fat content is much less influenced by environmental circumstances than selection for milk yield. In the Danish cow-testing associations, which cull all low-producing cows, average fat percentage of the milk increased steadily from 1905 to 1945, while milk yield was sharply depressed by feed shortage during the two world wars. This indicates that the genotype plays a larger role in the determination of fat content than in the determination of milk yield, a conclusion that had already been drawn from comparisons between the performances of related cows. In animal breeding research, as in human genetics (Chap. 17), comparisons between relatives of various degrees including—in cattle—identical and fraternal twins are used for assessing the relative contributions of heredity and environment to important characters. In contrast to the human geneticist, the animal geneticist can in large measure choose the environment of his test animals, and this makes his conclusions more reliable. The most direct measure of an animal's genetical merits is provided by the performance of its progeny, and progeny testing plays an important role in modern animal breeding. It is almost indispensable when the selected animal itself does not show the character under selection, as when dairy bulls are selected to improve milk performance of the herd. Although the pedigree of the bull may provide some assessment of his endowment with genes for milk production, the most reliable information comes from the performance of his daughters under controlled environmental conditions. Since these daughters are scattered over many different farms with different kinds of management, the performance of contemporary cows on the same farm is used as standard of comparison in each case. The selection of bulls for artificial insemination affects very large numbers of offspring, and progeny testing is here of special significance.

Even in cross-fertilized species, selection within a group is limited by its over-all content of genes. A particular strain may lack desirable genes that are present in another, or it may carry a desirable gene so closely linked to an undesirable one that it is practically impossible to separate the two. Such an impasse can be broken by crossbreeding, often called "hybridization." Crossbreeding, by bringing together genes from two sources, not only widens the scope for selection but may also produce new types that combine desirable qualities of different varieties. Thus, the winter-hardiness of one variety of wheat has been successfully combined with the high yield of another, and resistance to various kinds of diseases and pests has been combined in the same variety of beans. Crossbreeding has played an important role in the formation of our modern breeds of animals and is still used widely for the creation of new breeds; but once a breed is established and has proved its merit, its purity has to be preserved by avoiding further hybridization.

Hybridization in a very special sense forms the basis for the greatest practical success of modern genetics. This story will be told in the next chapter.

CHAPTER 22   *A Success Story: Hybrid Corn*

IT IS SOMETIMES NECESSARY to go backward in order to go forward in the end. In a simple psychological test, an animal and a small child are shown a desired object which can be reached only by a detour round a fence. A toddler understands quickly that he has to go away from the object before going toward it; a chicken never understands it. Plant breeding owes much to a man who realized this truth.

Under the influence of Johannsen's experiments with beans, G. H. Shull in the early years of this century tried to produce pure lines of maize by self-fertilization. Maize is not a naturally self-fertilizing crop like beans, and it does not take kindly to inbreeding. Generation after generation, the plants became smaller and weaker (Fig. 65) and the yield of kernels decreased correspondingly. From the viewpoint of practical corn breeding, this was a mad program, which seemed to lead farther and farther away from the desired goal of increased food production. But Shull was not interested in immediate practical success; he wanted pure lines for studying the genetics of grain yield, and he was willing to go backward on the way to what was ultimately to be a step forward.

As it turned out, the really important step forward in this program was not the genetical analysis of pure lines but the observation that crosses between the weak inbred strains produced plants that were superior not only to their parents but often also to the varieties from which the inbreds had originally been isolated

(Fig. 66). Shull, therefore, suggested that inbred lines should be produced and maintained for the sole purpose of utilizing their crossbred (hybrid) progeny.

"Inbreeding degeneration" and "hybrid vigor" were already known to Charles Darwin, who had carried out many experiments on inbreeding and crossbreeding. Other corn breeders in the United States started programs for improving maize production by crossing inbred lines. The results were spectacular beyond expectation.

In the early thirties hybrid seed was first released for agricultural purposes. From 1935 to 1957 the corn acreage planted with hybrid

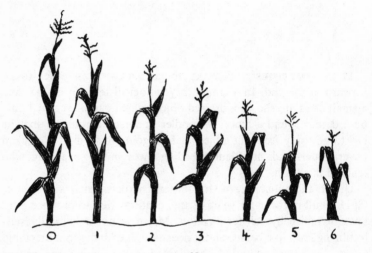

FIG. 65.
Inbreeding degeneration in corn.

seed in the United States increased from 1.1 to 92.5 per cent. At the same time the over-all acreage planted to corn went down, for each acre yielded more and more grain, so that 73,000 acres in 1957 yielded 50 per cent more grain than 100,000 acres in 1930. In 1943 it was estimated that the *increase* in corn yield due to the use of hybrid seed was 669,480,000 bushels; fed to pigs, this amount would have been sufficient to supply each man, woman and child in the nation with 54 pounds of pork. In 1947 the increased yield resulting from the use of hybrid seed was estimated as at least 800 million bushels. It is easy to imagine what these phenomenally increased food supplies meant during the difficult years of the war and the early postwar period. After the war the use of hybrid corn was introduced into many other countries, for instance, Italy, Mexico, Russia. Some, like Italy, can import American hybrid seed; others have to develop their own inbred lines from which hybrid corn adapted to local conditions can be obtained by crossing.

Hybrid corn is the outstanding practical success of modern genetics. Mendelian principles have all along been guiding lines for the scientists who launched the corn-breeding program. We shall

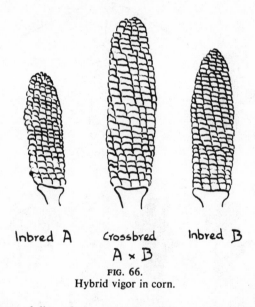

Inbred A   Crossbred   Inbred B
A × B

FIG. 66.
Hybrid vigor in corn.

now attempt to follow their reasoning and to explain both inbreeding degeneration and hybrid vigor on a genetical basis.

The most fundamental fact has already been mentioned in the previous chapter. It was stated there, without explanation (p. 176), that "continued self-fertilization gives individuals that are homozygous for all or almost all their genes." Why this should be so can be most easily understood from a simple example.

In the snapdragon, red or ivory flower color is due to a pair of allelomorphs neither of which is completely dominant over the other, so that the heterozygote has pinkish flowers. In nature, snapdragons are fertilized by bees; but this can be prevented by "bagging" the flowers so that they are inaccessible to foreign pollen. Figure 67 shows what happens when self-fertilization is practiced on a heterozygous, pink-flowered plant and its progeny. Following

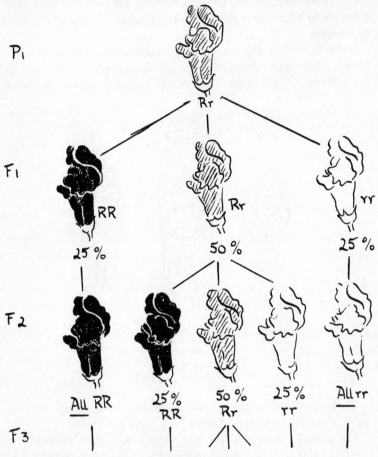

FIG. 67.
Increase in homozygosity through self-fertilization.

Mendel's first law (Chap. 6), the first generation segregates into 25 per cent homozygous red-flowered plants, 25 per cent homozygous ivory-flowered plants, and 50 per cent heterozygous pink-flowered plants. The very first act of self-fertilization, therefore, has immediately yielded 50 per cent homozygotes for one or the other allele. In the following generation produced by self-fertilization the progeny of the homozygotes will consist entirely of homozygotes, while the progeny of the heterozygotes will again segregate out 50 per cent homozygotes. So it will go on, the remaining proportion of heterozygotes dwindling rapidly with each generation of self-fertilization, until for all practical purposes heterozygotes have become negligible. But—and this is a most important point to remember—the homozygotes are of two different types; continued inbreeding of a line that starts with heterozygosity for one pair of alleles results in two homozygous lines.

What applies to one pair of alleles applies to all others; continued inbreeding will transform heterozygosity for any one of them into lines homozygous for one or the other. Suppose we start with a plant that is heterozygous for two pairs of alleles: *AaBb;* self-fertilization will result in lines that are homozygous for both pairs. Theoretically, four such lines are possible, namely, *AABB, AAbb, aaBB, aabb.* If the two genes are on different chromosomes, all four lines will be produced in approximately equal proportions according to Mendel's second law (Chap. 19). Even if the genes are linked (Chap. 20), crossing over will often allow the formation of all possible lines, although not in equal proportions. The greater the number of allelic pairs for which the original plant is heterozygous the greater the number of homozygous lines into which it will split under continued self-fertilization. Plants of naturally crosspollinated species are usually heterozygous for many genes, and after continued self-fertilization any such plant will give rise to many homozygous lines.

In terms of Mendelian genetics, therefore, continued self-fertilization gives an array of separate lines all of which are homozygous for combinations of alleles for which the first plant was heterozygous. It remains to ask why this should result in inbreeding degeneration. The answer was foreshadowed in Chapter 12, where it was shown that even the mild degree of inbreeding practiced in human populations may, in certain cases, result in "degeneration," as when cousins who are both heterozygous for the gene for amaurotic idiocy produce a homozygous affected child. In general, it is homozygosity for previously hidden harmful recessives that makes the inbred lines inferior to the parental strain.

So much for inbreeding degeneration. What about hybrid vigor or, as it is often called, "heterosis"? In a general way we may say that hybrid vigor derives from the restoration of heterozygosity by crossing. We have seen that even inbred lines developed from the same original plant will differ in the allele combinations for which they are homozygous; this applies to an even greater extent to inbred lines derived from different varieties of corn. Here, almost every line will owe its defectiveness to homozygosity for different recessive genes, and in the hybrids the dominants contributed by one parent will cover up the recessives received from the other. Suppose, for instance, that *a, b, c* and *d* are harmful recessives and that two inbred lines have the genotypes *AA bb cc dd* and *aa BB cc DD*. When these lines are crossed the hybrids will have the genotype *Aa Bb cc Dd,* that is, they will manifest the ill effects of only one of the genes as compared with the parents, which manifested the ill effects of two or three of them. Obviously the degree to which heterozygosity is restored by crossing and, with this, the degree of heterosis will depend on the choice of lines for crossing; in practice, many different crosses are tried out in attempts to find those lines that give the most valuable hybrids.

Since all plants of an inbred line are not only alike but also homozygous, there is no segregation when they form gametes, and all hybrids between two inbred lines have the same genotype. The hybrids start their life cycle as kernels on the inbred mother plants that have been fertilized by pollen from a different inbred line. Such kernels are much more uniform than kernels harvested from ordinary plants, and this has its use for certain purposes, for instance, in the canning of sweet corn. On the other hand, weak inbred plants yield few kernels, and it is therefore the rule for commercial hybrid seed to be harvested from the first-generation hybrids rather than directly from the inbred plants. The resulting loss in uniformity through segregation is not serious; but if a farmer goes on using seed from hybrid plants he will soon lose most of the advantages of hybrid corn through continued segregation. Farmers who grow hybrid corn have to purchase fresh hybrid seed for each sowing.

While there is general agreement that inbreeding and hybrid vigor arise largely in the way described here, some geneticists feel that this is not the whole explanation. They believe that the superior quality of heterozygotes is due not only to the covering up of harmful recessives but also to the presence of certain allele pairs that act best in heterozygous combination, *Aa* being superior to both *AA* and *aa*. In Chapter 23 we shall hear of a pair of human alleles where this is apparently true. Whether such cases are frequent and whether and how much they contribute to hybrid vigor is a presently much-debated question.

Programs for utilizing hybrid vigor in other branches of plant breeding have been started in various countries. For domestic animals, such attempts are beset with great difficulties: the impossibility of self-fertilization, the severe inbreeding degeneration after continued brother-sister matings, the small number of progeny, and the high monetary value of the individual animal. To reach anything even approaching homozygosity for all genes is out of the question. Nevertheless, even crosses between partly inbred lines may show hybrid vigor, and promising beginnings have been made with poultry, where the "hybrid chick" industry was started by Henry Wallace in the twenties and has already achieved marked popularity. Wallace marketed his first hybrid chicks in 1942 and is now selling yearly over 30 million of them. Similar attempts for pigs are under way.

A term that plays a great role in the literature on hybrid vigor is "nicking." By this is meant the particular ability of two lines to co-operate in the production of a vigorous hybrid, the defective genes of the one line being covered up by their dominant alleles in the other, and vice versa. I should like to finish this chapter with an example of nicking from human genetics. Deaf-mutism, as mentioned before (p. 90), is often due to a recessive gene. Genetical deaf-mutes are homozygous for such a gene, and when two of them marry all their children would be expected to be deaf. It is, therefore, surprising that not infrequently marriages between deaf partners result in hearing children. Occasionally, this is so because one or both of the parents are not genetically deaf, but have acquired deafness through some accident or illness. Other cases have a different explanation.

Normal hearing depends on the undisturbed interaction of many genes, and mutation in any one of these may lead to deafness. Let us consider two such genes, *D* and *E*. Normal persons are genotypically *DD EE,* deaf people are *dd EE* or *DD ee*. In addition, there are heterozygotes: *Dd EE,* or *DD Ee,* or *Dd Ee.* All of these are normal-hearing since both mutant genes are recessive to their normal allelomorphs. In a certain family the mutant gene *d* is transmitted, and cousin marriage results in the birth of a deaf girl, Pamela. Pamela's genotype is *dd EE.* She grows up in an institution for the deaf, together with her cousin Jack, who, as a member of the same family, most probably has the same gene for deafness as Pamela. Jack wishes to marry Pamela, but fortunately Pamela rejects his offer. There can be little doubt that all the children from this marriage would have been genotypically *dd EE* and phenotypically deaf like their parents. Instead, Pamela decides to marry another inmate of the institution, Henry. Henry comes from a family in which the gene *e* is transmitted, and his genotype is *DD ee.* While the gametes produced by Pamela carry the genes *d* and *E,* those produced by Henry carry the genes *D* and *e.* The genotype of the children is therefore *Dd Ee* and, to the delight of the family, all of them are hearing. This is a simple case of nicking.

The reader should now be able to understand a remark made in Chapter 7 in regard to mink breeding. It was said there that the recessive mutation "platinum" had occurred independently in two ranches, and that when animals from the two mutant strains were crossed together all their young were platinum. This, it was said, convinced the geneticists that the two mutations were the same. The reason for this conclusion should now be obvious. Had the two mutations been different, the young minks—like the children of Henry and Pamela—would have been heterozygous for both of them and nicking would have suppressed the manifestation of either.

Nicking can occur in all cases where different mutant genes produce the same phenotypical abnormality. Such cases are exceedingly frequent; in the next chapter we shall see why this is so.

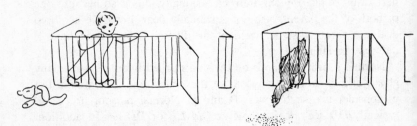

CHAPTER **23** *Genes and*
Characters

THERE IS HARDLY ANY CHARACTER in any organism that is not to some extent under the influence of the genotype. Genes control the colors and shapes of animals and plants, the ability of animals to see, hear and smell, the resistance of a man to an infecting bacterium, and the ability of the bacterium to infect the man. They influence the rate at which a calf will grow on a given diet, the degree to which a child can profit from education, and the likelihood that a person's balance of mind will give way under mental stress. They determine whether or not a Chlamydomonas has flagellae for swimming about, and whether or not a yeast culture can grow on galactose (Chap. 5). Genes influence the most superficial as well as the most fundamental processes of life; they act at every stage of development. Indeed, the very chance of survival at any period from conception to extreme old age is to some degree under the control of the genotype. In chickens, rats and mice, mutant genes have been shown to kill the embryo by severely disturbing the development of such vital organs as the skeleton, the brain, the kidneys. Doubtless, the normal alleles of these genes play a role in controlling the normal development of these organs. Equally doubtless, similar genes will play this role in the human embryo. At the other end of the life span we find that inbred lines of mice differ in the average length of life of the individual. There is little reason to doubt that also in man longevity is in part gene-determined, although the very great genetical and environmental variability among human individuals makes it difficult to provide conclusive evidence for it.

It seems that the great majority of genes are indispensable for the survival of the organism. In experimental animals or plants, very small pieces of chromosome can be destroyed by, for instance, X rays. (Chap. 4, Figs. 3 and 4). Attempts to breed individuals that lack the same piece in both partner chromosomes rarely are successful; for no matter which piece is missing, it almost invariably seems to contain genes without which survival is impossible. In Drosophila, it could be shown that even genes controlling such a seemingly irrelevant character as eye color or shape of wing margin need to be present in at least one chromosome for the embryo to develop into a living fly. If such genes had no other effects than their easily observed ones, this would be difficult to understand. There is, however, ample evidence that most, if not all, genes produce a variety of effects.

This evidence comes from a study of mutant genes. The very existence of a normal gene can be inferred only after it has mutated at least once, and its effects must be deduced from a comparison between normal and mutated individuals. Many mutant genes have several obvious effects. In Drosophila, the mutant gene "lozenge" makes the eyes look sticky like boiled sweets, removes the claws and pads from the feet so that the flies can no longer walk up the glass wall of their culture bottle, and makes the females infertile. Japanese waltzing mice are deaf; Frizzle hens (Chap. 16) have immature ovaries and lay few eggs. It is safe to conclude that the normal allelomorphs of these genes are necessary for the normal development of eyes, feet, and genetical organs in Drosophila; of ears and nervous system in mice; of plumage and ovaries in fowl. Whenever a mutant gene is studied thoroughly, it is found to produce a whole array of effects. Most mutant genes reduce viability; it is therefore not surprising that their normal alleles are necessary for life. The ability of a gene to produce several distinct effects is called "pleiotropy," that is, "many-directedness." From what has been said just now it is clear that pleiotropy is the rule and not the exception.

Just as every gene influences many characters, so is every character influenced by many genes; this is known as "gene interaction." In a way, gene interaction and pleiotropy are complementary to each other; for to state that many genes act pleiotropically on viability is only a different way of saying that viability is influenced by many genes. Similarly, many mutant genes and, by inference, their normal alleles affect fertility and, conversely, fertility depends

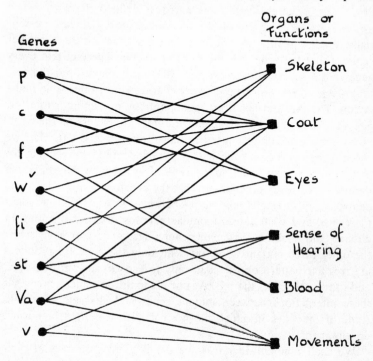

Abbreviations

P = pink, c = albino, f = flexed tail
W^v = dominant spotting, fi = fidget, st = shaker-short
Va = varitint waddler, v = waltzer

FIG. 68.
Genes and characters in the house mouse.

on the action of all these genes as well as on that of others which do not advertise their presence by striking effects on superficial characters. Even very specific characters, like the color of the iris in the human eye, depend on the action of many genes.

Figure 68 illustrates this complementary relationship between pleiotropy and gene interaction for a few mutant genes of the house mouse. In order to avoid details, the "characters" have been chosen as broadly as possible and might better be called "organs" or "functions." The choice of more narrowly defined characters, such as eye color or structure of the tail, would have yielded an essentially similar picture. A line connecting a gene with a character signifies that the gene influences the character. The fact that every gene is the source of several lines illustrates pleiotropy; the fact that several lines terminate in every character illustrates gene interaction. The diagram has been kept simple by restricting it to a few genes and characters. Had we entered more characters on the right, more lines would have started in most genes on the left. Had we entered more genes on the left, more lines would have come together in most characters on the right. The irregular way in which the lines cross each other shows that the constellation of characters controlled by a single gene varies between genes. Thus the genes *fi, st, Va,* and *v* all cause a similar nervous disorder resulting in circling and shaking movements; but fidget mice can hear, while the other three mutant types are deaf; only the gene *Va* produces an irregular pattern on the coat, only *fi* leads to sores in the eyes, and only *st* shortens the tail. Again, it should be remembered that these interactions between mutant genes and characters indicate some of the ways in which the normal alleles interact in normal development.

We shall now consider in some detail a few examples of pleiotropy and gene interaction. When we have done this we shall realize what a crude and vastly oversimplified picture is presented in Fig. 68.

I. PLEIOTROPY: ONE GENE AFFECTS SEVERAL CHARACTERS

(a) *Sickle-cell anemia.* In 1910 a young West Indian Negro consulted an American physician about a feverish cold. Since he complained of not having felt well for quite a long time, the doctor undertook a thorough examination, in the course of which he found that the young man suffered from severe anemia of a hitherto not recorded type. Under the microscope his blood presented a striking picture (Fig. 69a). While in normal blood the red cells are uniformly round disks, the blood of the patient contained a high

proportion of curiously sickle-shaped red cells. Several years later
the same abnormality was found in the blood of a father and his
son, both suffering from anemia. The condition was called "sickle-

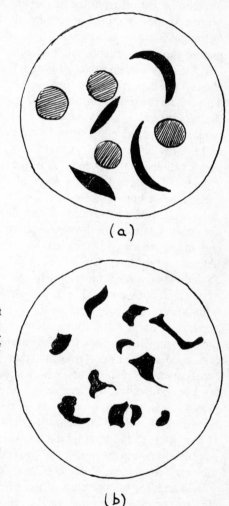

(a)

FIG. 69.
Blood corpuscles of a patient
with sickle-cell anemia. In (b)
the sickling has been empha-
sized by keeping the drop of
blood sealed off from the air.

(b)

cell anemia"; it is quite distinct from the more usual forms of
anemia. Once attention had been directed to it, more cases were
reported, at first exclusively from Negroes. It soon became obvious
that the disease was in some way hereditary, but its accurate genet-

ical basis was determined only when a technique had been developed that ensured reliable detection of the sickling phenomenon. This technique consists in keeping the sample of blood for a day or more sealed off from the air, when the cells of patients assume bizarre shapes, some of which are shown in Fig. 69b. With this technique it was established that, in addition to the typical blood picture found in patients suffering from sickle-cell anemia, a mild, but distinctly recognizable form of sickling occurs in the blood of about 9 per cent American Negroes who do not suffer from anemia. This milder, harmless form of sickling is especially frequent among the relatives of patients suffering from sickle-cell anemia; in particular, it is practically always found in both parents of an anemic child. This led to the interpretation, fully borne out by further investigations, that the condition is due to a gene S, which in heterozygotes $S+$ causes the mild form of sickling, unaccompanied by anemia, while homozygotes SS are anemic.

Laboratory investigations of the abnormal blood revealed that the gene S affects the hemoglobin, that is, the pigmented, iron-containing protein of the red blood cells. In an electric field like the one shown in Fig. 33 the hemoglobin molecules of SS individuals move more slowly than the hemoglobin molecules of normal individuals. The blood of heterozygotes $S+$ contains both kinds of hemoglobin in approximately equal proportions; apparently one kind is formed under the influence of the S gene, the other under the influence of its normal allele. This, incidentally, is a good illustration of the fact that the terms "dominant" and "recessive" are relative, and that a gene may be dominant at one level of observation and recessive at another. At the level of hemoglobin chemistry, the gene S and its normal allelomorph act independently of each other, similar to the blood group genes A and B (Chap. 10); at the level of the microscopic blood picture, S is incompletely dominant over its normal allele; finally, at the level of the manifest disease, S is recessive to its normal allele.

A search for the presence of the gene S in many countries gave curious results. At first it seemed as though the gene was restricted to Negroes, in Africa and in the two Americas. Later, individuals whose blood could be made to sickle were found also among Italians, Greeks, and other peoples around the Mediterranean, and among South Indian tribes. The distribution of such individuals, however, was exceedingly patchy. While large numbers of them occurred in certain parts of Africa, they were practically absent from others. Even within the same territory there often were striking differences in the proportion of individuals with sickle cells. In Uganda, for example, this proportion was nearly one half in one tribe and nearly zero in another.

The most puzzling aspect of this survey was that sicklers $(S+)$ have such high frequencies in certain populations. Homozygotes for S rarely reach adulthood and have children; nature effectively sterilizes them. Although, as we saw in Chapter 13, sterilization of homozygotes for a recessive gene is a very inefficient way of getting rid of the gene, it will keep its frequency low. In fact, other genes that result in "natural sterilization" of the homozygotes, such as the gene for amauritic idiocy, are rare even in heterozygotes. It therefore seemed that in certain populations the childless death of the homozygotes was overbalanced by the fact that the heterozygotes had some natural advantage which gave them a better chance than the rest of the population to have children, half of whom would inherit the gene S.

A possible clue to the nature of this advantage was provided by the discovery that sicklers are frequent in malaria-ridden regions and are rare or absent in malaria-free regions. This suggested that the gene S in some way protects its carriers against the malaria parasite. Investigations to test this idea lent support to it. Out of 288 young children in a malaria district of Africa, 43 were heterozygous for S and of these 12, that is, 28 per cent, were found to carry the malaria parasite in their blood; of the remaining 245 children, all without the gene S, 113, that is, 46 per cent, carried the parasite. In one African tribe 30 volunteers offered themselves for infection with malaria; 15 of them were $S+$ and of these only 2 contracted the disease; the other 15 were $++$, and of these only 1 remained free of it.

Altogether, there is good, although not yet wholly conclusive, evidence for a pleiotropic effect of the gene S. The same altered hemoglobin that in homozygotes results in anemia makes the blood of heterozygotes an unsuitable environment for the malaria parasite. Since malaria affects physical and mental development in various ways, the final pleiotropic effects of a gene controlling susceptibility to this disease will be correspondingly far-reaching.

If this explanation of the curious distribution of the gene S is correct, we are dealing with a case in which a heterozygote for two alleles ($S+$) is superior to the homozygotes for either (SS or $++$). In Chapter 22 this situation has been mentioned as a possible contributory cause of hybrid vigor.

(b) *Hereditary dwarfism in the mouse.* In 1929 a few dwarf mice appeared in the mouse colony of Harvard University (Plate V, 2). They did not breed, but when their littermates were bred together, some of the litters contained about one quarter dwarf mice. The character thus was attributed to the action of a recessive gene. Mice homozygous for this gene stop growing at the end of the second week or a little later and usually reach a weight of only 6–8 grams as compared with a weight of 20 grams or more for normal mice. Plate V, 2, shows an adult dwarf mouse together with its normal littermate. The dwarf gene has many pleiotropic effects (Fig. 70). Early on in development, even before growth has stopped, homozygotes can be distinguished from their normal littermates by blunt snouts and relatively shorter ears and tails. At the stage when normal young mice are lively and easily excited, dwarf mice are timid and quiet. They are very sensitive to temperature changes; but when they are kept at the right temperature they tolerate starvation better than normal mice. They have a shortened life span and are sterile in both sexes. Examination of their inner organs revealed that most of their hormone producing glands, such as the thyroid, the pituitary, and the gonads, were undersized and abnormal in structure. Now, it is well known that the pituitary, a small gland at the base of the skull, occupies a key position in the control of hormone production; for this reason it is often referred to as "the master gland." It therefore occurred to some scientists to attempt to cure the hereditary dwarfism by treatment with pituitary.

Pieces of fresh rat pituitary were implanted daily under the skin of dwarf mice which had stopped growing. The success of the treatment was spectacular. The treated animals attained normal weight and body proportions, they became lively and vigorous and behaved in every way like normal mice. The males became fertile, but the females remained sterile, although their ovaries regained normal size and structure. Similarly, all other hormone-producing glands, with one notable exception, became normal. The exceptional gland, which did not respond to the treatment, was the pituitary. This is exactly what one would expect if the basic defect, from which all the others are derived, is an abnormality of the master gland; for, while implanted pituitary can supply all the hormones by which a normal pituitary controls its subordinate glands, it cannot cure the source of the trouble in the pituitary itself.

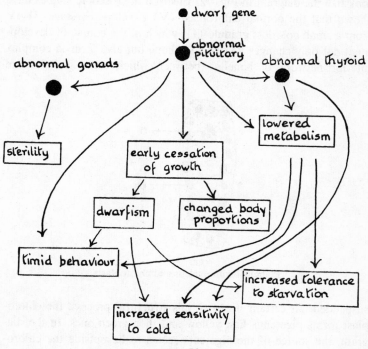

FIG. 70.
Pleiotropic effects of the dwarf gene in the mouse.

II. GENE INTERACTION: ONE CHARACTER DEPENDS ON MANY GENES

(a) *Chlorophyll formation.* In the cells of green plants the green pigments, together with some yellow ones, are carried inside numerous small bodies, the so-called "chloroplasts" (Fig. 71). Primitive plants, for instance, algae, may have one large chloroplast instead. Before the invention of the electron microscope, not much detail could be discerned in a chloroplast. Nowadays electron micrographs (Plate VI, 1) reveal a highly complicated structure. Combined with genetical studies observations with the electron microscope have become an important tool for understanding the role of the genes in the development of the chloroplast, and although this work is still at its beginning, a rough picture of gene interaction has started to emerge. Its details are still largely unknown; but it is likely that in its broad features it will turn out to look like the diagram in Fig. 72. Electron microscopic studies have shown that the normal chloroplast (V) develops by stages II–IV from a small colorless granule (I), which in the course of development not only changes its size and shape but also forms a complex interior network of lamellae between which some globules are

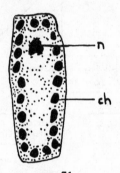

FIG. 71.
Plant cell with nucleus and chloroplasts.

suspended. At certain stages of this structural process, the chloroplast forms pigments, first yellow and then green ones. In the diagram, the source of the pigments seems to lie outside the chloroplast; this has been done for the sake of clarity: in reality, the pigments form inside the chloroplast. It is certain that a vast number of genes are involved in the control of these processes, for many different mutations have been shown to interfere with chlorophyll and chloroplast formation. More than a hundred such genes have proclaimed their existence by mutation; many more may have remained undetected because they have not yet given rise to observed mutations. It is also known that different genes control different steps of chlorophyll formation; for mutations may arrest chloroplast development at different stages and in different ways.

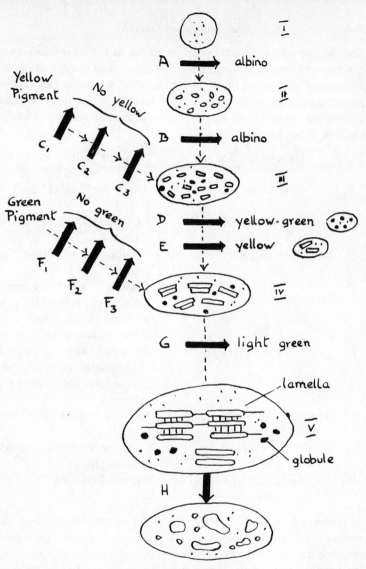

bleached

I–V = stages in development of the normal chloroplast
A–G = genes or groups of genes controlling chloroplast development
➡ = blocks in developmental processes
  H = gene required for persistence of normal chloroplast. Mutation
      results in degeneration.

FIG. 72.
A—partly hypothetical—diagram of the genetic control of
chlorophyll synthesis.

The diagram shows a number of genes (A to G) whose existence has been inferred in this manner. In addition, a gene (H) has been entered which has no effect on chlorophyll formation but whose presence appears to be required for survival of the fully formed chloroplast; mutation of this gene results in destruction ("bleaching") of the chloroplast.

Gene	Gene-controlled step	Loss of activity of gene results in
A	I into II	Albino seedling, chloroplast stage I
B	II into III	Albino seedling, chloroplast stage II
C	Formation of yellow pigments	Seedling lacking yellow pigments
D	III into IV	Seedling with abnormal chloroplasts stage III, able to form some green pigment: yellow-green
E	III into IV	Seedling with abnormal chloroplasts stage III, unable to form green pigment: yellow
F	Formation of green pigments	Seedling lacking green pigments: yellow
G	IV into V	Light-green seedling, chloroplasts stage IV
H	Persistence of normal chloroplast	Bleached seedling

Several points should be noted: (1) The genes controlling the structure of the chloroplast (A, B, D, E, G) act in series, each gene carrying on where the previous one left off. Thus the gene B comes into action only after A has functioned; when the chloroplast, because of a mutated gene A, has been arrested in stage I, gene B and all following genes cannot function. (2) In the diagram it has been assumed that the same is true for the genes controlling the formation of yellow and green pigments ($C_1, C_2, C_3; F_1, F_2, F_3$). So far there is not much evidence for this assumption; but it is true for pigment formation in other organisms and is likely to be true also in the present case. (3) The different gene-controlled chains of development are interdependent. Pigment production starts when structural development has reached stage III, and it continues until stage V. Chloroplasts whose structural development has been arrested at stage III can form yellow pigment; whether they also can form at least a little amount of green pigment depends on the type of degenerative change they have undergone (mutation of D or E). It is also possible that a link exists between the two chains for pigment formation. (4) In normal development, the various chains interlink, and all of them contribute to the final product, the green chloroplast V.

Before we leave this example of gene interaction, it is well to point out that chloroplasts have an individuality of their own and are not wholly under the control of genes. A chloroplast, like the cell of which it forms a part, makes new chloroplasts by division, and a cell that has lost its chloroplasts cannot replace them. Sometimes a chloroplast may lose its ability to form pigment even in a cell containing all the requisite genes: the genes are ready to function, but the chloroplast cannot respond. Such a white chloroplast gives rise to a clone of white ones. When this happens early in the development of a plant, a whole shoot may become white, and cuttings from such a shoot also are white. This is a reminder that the genes, although indispensable for life and development, do not have an exclusive monopoly in the control of development. We shall come back to this in Chapter 28.

(b) *Genes acting in series: an illustration from human life.* Genes, like A, B, D, G or C_1, C_2, C_3 or F_1, F_2, F_3 in Fig. 72, that act in series resemble workers at a conveyer belt; nonfunctioning genes of such a series resemble absentee workers. Let us see what happens in a factory production line when one of the workers is absent. Figure 73 shows the assembly of a doll by four girls working at a conveyer belt. Ann has a supply of dolls' heads and fastens them to the bodies which are sent to her on the belt. She sends her product to Beryl, who adds the arms. Beryl sends her product to Cathie, who adds the legs. Cathie sends her product to Dot, who dresses the doll and puts the finished product into a box. Let us suppose that no worker can carry out any other manipulation than her own and, moreover, that she can do this only when the previous manipulations have been completed. This might, for instance,

FIG. 73.
Assembly of a doll on a conveyor belt.

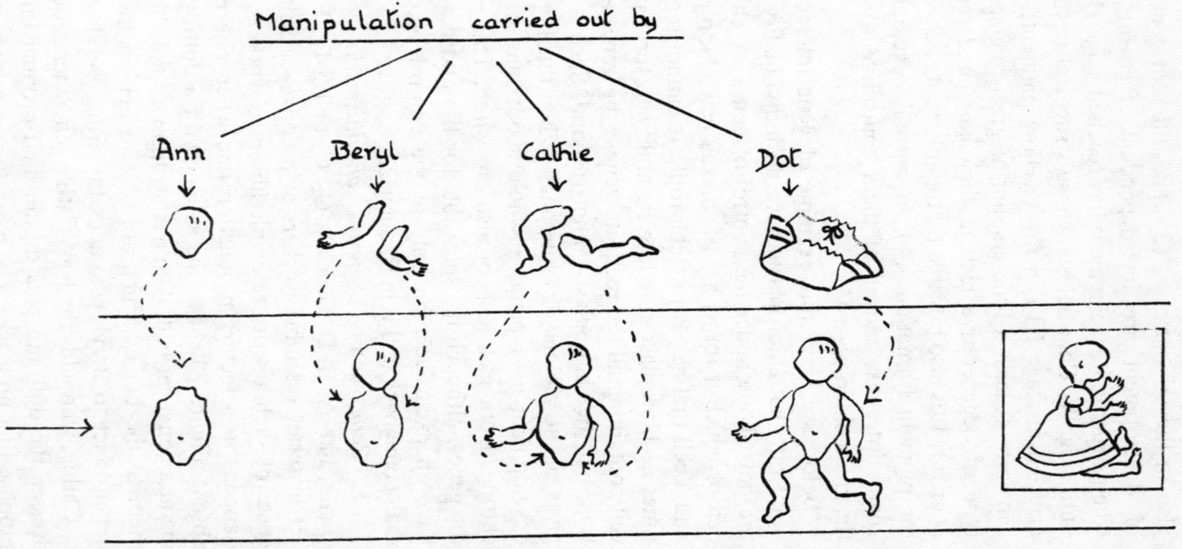

Manipulation carried out by

Ann   Beryl   Cathie   Dot

happen if the various parts of the body were attached to each other by strings with hooks which could be used in only one order. Now consider what happens when Ann is absent. If the conveyer belt is not stopped, headless and limbless bodies pass Ann's place, and since they cannot be manipulated by the other workers they accumulate at the end. If, instead, Beryl is absent, Ann will be able to carry out her manipulation but Cathie and Dot will not, and limbless bodies with heads will accumulate at the end of the line. Cathie's absence will result in an accumulation of legless bodies, and Dot's absence in an accumulation of naked but otherwise complete dolls. In general, when a worker is absent there will be an accumulation of the unfinished product furnished by the preceding worker.

Suppose now that the foreman of the production line is anxious to fulfill his quota of finished dolls and that he has the chance of obtaining either the finished product or the intermediate ones from a parallel production line which has a surplus of all of them. The finished product will, of course, help him in any case; but in order to keep the remainder of the workers occupied he may prefer to ask for an unfinished one. A look at Fig. 73 shows that this is not possible when Dot is the absentee; for she is the only one who can dress the doll. When Cathie is absent, Dot can be occupied by a supply of naked dolls, but Ann and Beryl will have to remain idle. When Beryl is absent, Dot can again be occupied by a supply of naked dolls; but now it would be preferable to obtain the previous product, legless dolls, for this would keep both Cathie and Dot busy. Finally, when the absentee is Ann, all remaining girls can be occupied if Beryl is supplied with limbless bodies; failing this, Cathie and Dot can be kept busy by a supply of legless bodies, or Dot alone by a supply of naked but otherwise complete dolls. In general, then, the choice between usable outside supplies is the greater the earlier along the line the absence occurred; when the last worker is absent only the finished product will do; when the first worker is absent all unfinished ones with the exception of the first will serve the purpose.

With this illustration in mind, we shall now discuss two examples of genes acting in series:

(c) *Synthesis of an amino acid by a bacterium.* One of the main constituents of living matter is protein. A protein molecule is a long chain of simpler organic molecules, called "amino acids." About twenty different amino acids are known to occur in proteins, and most organisms require all or most of them for life. Higher organisms like man obtain their amino acids through the protein in their diet. Many microorganisms, for instance most bacteria, can make or "synthesize" at least some of the required amino acids from simple inorganic ingredients of their food. Where genetical methods could be employed in the study of amino acid synthesis— and we shall see in Chapter 25 that even bacteria can be studied genetically—it was found that amino acid synthesis proceeds in

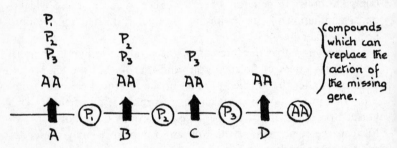

A, B, C, D = normal genes controlling successive steps in the synthesis of

AA = an amino acid

P_1, P_2, P_3 = intermediate products; precursors of AA

⬆ = block in the reaction series where one of the genes is not functioning

FIG. 74.
Gene-controlled stepwise synthesis of an amino acid.

steps, each step being controlled by a different gene. These genes, then, act in series like the girls at the conveyer belt. Our analysis of the "synthesis" of a doll will help us understand what happens when one of these genes mutates to an inactive state.

Figure 74 is a generalized diagram, applicable to many special cases, of four steps in the synthesis of an amino acid. Gene *A*, comparable to Ann in Fig. 73, synthesizes the first step; gene *B*, comparable to Beryl, synthesizes the second; gene *C*, comparable to Cathie, synthesizes the third, and *D*, comparable to Dot, the fourth. AA, comparable to the dressed doll, is the finished amino acid; P_1, P_2, and P_3 are three intermediate products, or "precursors," comparable to the three unfinished stages of the doll. Bacteria in which D is not functioning can survive only when they are supplied with the finished amino acid; for D, like Dot, is the only one that can carry out the final step. Bacteria with an inactive gene C can survive on either the amino acid or its precursor P_3. Bacteria with an inactive gene B can use not only the amino acid and P_3 but also P_2. Finally, bacteria in which A is not functioning can use all three precursors as well as the amino acid. Often such mutant strains accumulate precursors which precede the break in the production line; thus a strain with an inactive gene B may accumulate P_1, or a strain with an inactive gene D, P_3.

The study of chemical reactions in the living organism is called "biochemistry." The study of genes controlling biochemical reactions is called "biochemical genetics." The biochemical genetics of microorganisms has cleared up the manner in which many important compounds are synthesized under the control of genes acting in series. There is a remarkable similarity in the biochemical pathways by which cells of widely differing organisms synthesize essential compounds such as amino acids and vitamins, and the biochemical genetics of microorganisms has contributed at least as much to biochemical as to genetical knowledge.

(d) *A gene-controlled biochemical sequence in man.* Lastly we shall consider an example from human genetics where genes have been shown to work in series not on the synthesis but on the breakdown of an amino acid. In 1908 an English physician, Garrod, published a book called *Inborn Errors of Metabolism*. In it he dealt with a number of inherited disorders of human metabolism, that is, of those biochemical processes by which the living organism synthesizes new compounds or breaks down existing ones. One of the conditions described by Garrod was alkaptonuria, an abnormality characterized by a blackening of the urine and a blackening and hardening of the cartilage (gristle). The disease is inherited as a recessive autosomal (Chap. 15) condition and must therefore be due to the malfunctioning of a single gene. When the urine of patients was analyzed it was found to contain a substance called alkapton, which is absent from the urine of normal persons. Now alkapton is one of the breakdown products of protein, or rather of one particular amino acid, called "phenylalanine." When patients were given extra quantities of this amino acid in their diet, they excreted correspondingly more alkapton in their urine, while normal persons did not do so. In metabolism, phenylalanine is in the last resort broken down to carbon dioxide (CO_2) and water (H_2O). It appears that alkapton is an intermediate product in this chain of breakdown reactions, and that the gene for alkaptonuria interrupts the chain just after this stage has been reached. We may infer that the normal allele of the gene carries out the step that follows on the formation of alkapton.

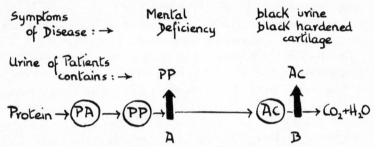

A = normal gene whose mutation results in phenylketonuria
B = normal gene whose mutation results in alkaptonuria
PA = phenylalanine, an amino acid
PP = phenylpyruvic acid
Ac = alkapton

FIG. 75.
Gene-controlled steps in the breakdown of an amino acid
(phenylalanine) in man.

Subsequently, a second gene—likewise autosomal and recessive —was found to intervene in the same chain of metabolic reactions, but at an earlier step. In this case, the mutation that led to the discovery of the gene has very serious effects; for homozygous individuals suffer from an extreme type of mental deficiency. The urine of these individuals contains large amounts of a substance called "phenylpyruvic acid," and the disease is called "phenyl-pyruvic idiocy" or "phenylketonuria" (Chap. 13). In the metabolism of phenylalanine, phenylpyruvic acid is the first breakdown product. In patients it is, therefore, the first step in the metabolic reaction chain that is blocked by the mutated gene; in normal individuals, it is the first step that is mediated by the normal allele. The whole story, as far as it has been discussed here, is set out diagrammatically in Fig. 75.

Conclusion. If, after this discussion of pleiotropy and gene inter-action, we look back at Fig. 68 we shall realize that the straight lines connecting genes and organs will have to be replaced by a network of intermediate reactions such as has been indicated in Fig. 76. Even this diagram gives only the very crudest idea of the

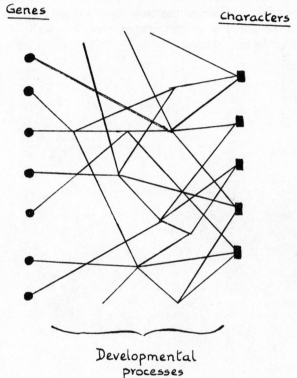

Genes   Characters

Developmental
processes

FIG. 76.
An improved diagram of genes and characters.

exceedingly intricate manner in which gene-controlled reactions interact in the production of a given phenotype. Obviously, the complexity of the network connecting a given character with an array of genes will differ between characters. It will be much greater for, say, body size in the mouse than for the presence of a given amino acid in a bacterium. If we go far enough back in the biochemical analysis of a given chain of developmental processes we should eventually reach a compound that is an immediate product of a given gene, connected with it by one single step. In Fig. 76 this has been expressed by having only *one* line originating from each gene. Pleiotropy, which in Fig. 68 seems to be a property of the genes themselves, is here seen to occur later as a consequence of the manifold connection between gene-controlled reactions. The search for the immediate products of the genes is one of the most active concerns of modern genetics. We shall hear more about it in the next chapter.

CHAPTER 24　　*What the Gene Does*

IN FIG. 74 THE genes are seen to control individual steps in the synthesis of an amino acid. It might be thought that here our analysis has come close to the immediate gene action, and according to modern genetical thought this is indeed likely.

The compounds that control individual steps in the synthesis or breakdown of an organic molecule, say an amino acid or a sugar, are called enzymes. Enzymes are proteins of a very special kind. Unlike other proteins in the living cell, they are not used as building blocks for making new living matter or for replacement of worn-out molecules; neither are they used as fuel for the production of the energy that is required for the sustenance of life. Yet none of the characteristic functions of the living organism—its growth, its metabolism, even its decay—can take place without enzymes. Biochemical reactions that by themselves occur so slowly that they often cannot even be detected are speeded up enormously in the presence of the appropriate enzyme. The enzyme itself is not used up in this process and may therefore be present in exceedingly small amounts. Enzymes are highly specific in regard to the reaction that they control. Just as an antibody "fits" only one particular antigen (Chap. 10, Fig. 20), so an enzyme speeds up only that particular biochemical reaction for which its chemical configuration fits it. Each step in the synthesis (Fig. 74) or breakdown (Fig. 75) of a particular amino acid is controlled by its own specific enzyme, and different amino acids require different arrays of enzymes for synthesis or breakdown.

When a gene can be shown to control a specific biochemical

reaction, the most plausible assumption is that it does so by controlling the production of the requisite enzyme. In a number of cases this has, indeed, been found to be true. Mutant strains that are blocked in some particular step of a chain-wise biochemical process (Fig. 74) often can be shown to lack the required enzyme or to possess, instead, an abnormal one.

Some interesting examples for the genic control of enzymes come from the study of "inborn errors of metabolism" in man (Chap. 23, p. 205). Alcaptonurics and phenylpyruvic idiots (Fig. 75) are deficient in one or the other of two enzymes involved in the breakdown of the amino acid phenylalanine. Another inborn error, inherited as an autosomal recessive condition, is the inability to digest galactose, one of the components of milk sugar. Infants that are homozygous for the responsible mutant gene resemble the mutant strains of yeast discussed in Chapter 5 (Fig. 9), which fail to grow on galactose, but grow well on glucose. The affected children not only do not thrive on milk; they also develop serious disturbances. Their liver becomes enlarged, they develop cataract, and mental development is retarded. They improve rapidly on a milk-free diet, but if the change in diet happens too late some of the damage is already beyond repair. It has been found that such infants lack one of the enzymes by which galactose is transformed into glucose. Precisely how this results not only in stunted growth but also in definite abnormalities is not known; probably lack of glucose as well as the accumulation of toxic substances play a role. The parents of affected children, who presumably are carriers of the gene, form markedly less enzyme than do normal individuals. This might give genetic counselors (Chap. 12) the means for preventing the birth of affected children in families in which the mutant gene is carried. The great similarity of biochemical patterns throughout the realm of living organisms is illustrated by the fact that affected children lack precisely the same enzyme that is lacking in certain strains of bacteria which fail to grow on galactose. Other strains of bacteria cannot grow on galactose because they lack one of the other enzymes necessary for the transformation of galactose into glucose.

Another gene-controlled enzyme activity was detected recently when new antimalarial drugs were introduced into medical practice. It was then discovered that certain persons react to these drugs by developing a severe anemia; curiously enough, the eating of broad beans (fava beans) produces the same symptoms in these individuals. This last fact had already been discovered a little earlier in Israel, where the condition was called "favism." Inheritance of this abnormal reaction to beans and certain drugs appears to be sex-linked, with partial dominance in heterozygous women. The root of the abnormality was tracked down to an unusually low activity of an enzyme contained in the red blood corpuscles. This in turn alters the chemical composition of the blood corpuscles so that they are more easily destroyed by certain drugs or foodstuffs.

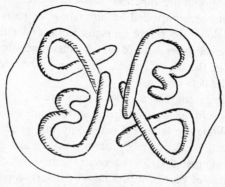

FIG. 77.
A diagrammatic representation of the structure of hemoglobin.

Enzymes are only one group of proteins, albeit a highly important one. Other proteins are equally essential for life; in fact, proteins together with nucleic acids (Chap. 25) are the most important constituents of living matter. The most impressive evidence for the genic control of protein synthesis comes not from studies of enzymes but from investigations on hereditary differences in hemoglobin, the protein of the red blood corpuscles. We saw in Chapter 23 (p. 194) that individuals with the mutant gene for sickling (S) have an altered kind of hemoglobin. The chemical nature of this alteration has been established by ingenious methods of analysis. The large molecule of hemoglobin consists of two identical half-molecules. Each half-molecule, in turn, consists of two chains of amino acids, one of which has been called alpha chain, the other beta chain (Fig. 77). Each chain is composed of about 140 amino acids, and the arrangement of the amino acids in the alpha chain differs from that in the beta chain. The difference between normal hemoglobin and mutant hemoglobin *S* was found to reside in one single amino acid in one particular spot of the two beta chains. Another abnormal hemoglobin, *C,* likewise under the control of a single gene, differs from normal by having still a different amino acid in the same spot of the beta chains. As would be expected, the genetical evidence indicates that the genes for hemoglobin *S* and hemoglobin *C* are allelic. Other abnormal hemoglobins have changes in single amino acids at some other spot of the alpha or beta chains. Genetical studies of families in which two abnormal types of hemoglobin are inherited show that changes in the alpha and beta chains are controlled by different gene pairs. The formation of hemoglobin, therefore, appears to be under the control of two series of gene pairs, one of which determines the sequence of amino acids in the alpha chains, while the other determines the sequence in the beta chains.

These findings suggest a much more precise picture of gene action than could be derived from a study of inherited enzyme differences. While the latter indicates only that genes are involved in the production of enzyme proteins, the results obtained with hemoglobins suggest that a gene controls the formation of a particular protein—or part of a protein—by determining its sequence of amino acids. If we denote the 20 common amino acids arbitrarily by the first 20 letters of the alphabet, one gene might, for instance, determine a sequence that starts with the letters RED, while its allele determines an otherwise identical chain that starts with the letters ROD. If this picture of gene action—or at least of the action of certain genes—is correct, we have to consider these genes as carriers of a code for protein formation, and the first steps in gene action would be the decoding of this information and its translation into "letters" spelled by amino acids. So far this is not more than a hypothesis, but it is a hypothesis that agrees well with many experimental findings. In this chapter we have reviewed some of the evidence gained from analyzing the products of gene action; in the next chapter we shall consider the evidence gained from an analysis of the chemical nature of the genes.

CHAPTER 25 *What the Gene Is*

CHROMOSOMES CONSIST OF a substance called nucleoprotein. Nucleoprotein is made up of two components, protein and nucleic acid. The nucleic acid is of a particular type, called desoxyribonucleic acid or, for short, DNA. A different kind of nucleic acid, called ribonucleic acid or RNA, is found in the cytoplasm, in certain viruses and, to a small extent, in the chromosomes. Until fairly recently, the protein was regarded as the essential genetical component of the chromosomes, mainly because it is a more complex substance than nucleic acid and therefore seemed more suited for the transfer of complex instructions to the cytoplasm. In particular, it was considered possible that these instructions were carried by protein molecules that, like molecules of antigen (Fig. 20), were folded into specific configurations. A series of spectacular discoveries during the past fourteen years has induced geneticists to change their ideas and to consider DNA as the main constituent of the gene. In what follows we shall go briefly over some of the evidence that led to this reversal of opinion. This will take us into strange new fields of research, concerned with viruses and bacteriophages, and with the sex life of bacteria. We shall not proceed in historical order of discovery, but shall advance from the more easily understood findings to the more complicated ones.

TOBACCO MOSAIC VIRUS

Plate VI, 2, shows three tobacco leaves; the left leaf is healthy, the others are suffering from a disease called mosaic disease. This disease is highly infectious and may spread rapidly through a plantation. Toward the end of the nineteenth century it was found that a healthy tobacco plant can be infected by the juice of a diseased one, even when the juice has previously been passed through a filter of unglazed porcelain which holds back all bacteria. Soon afterward it was shown that also the infectious agent of foot-and-mouth disease can pass through filters that retain bacteria. Infectious agents of this type were called "filterable viruses"; the world "filterable" has meanwhile been dropped as unnecessary.

Before the advent of the electron miscroscope, only the largest viruses could be seen at the highest possible magnification, and then only as tiny dots. Nowadays the electron microscope yields beautiful pictures of even the smallest viruses. Plate VII, 1, is an electron micrograph of tobacco mosaic virus particles.

Chemically, viruses consist of nucleoprotein. Some viruses, like the genes of higher organisms, have DNA for their nucleic acid component; others have RNA instead. The tobacco mosaic virus belongs in the latter group. Its protein is shaped like a hollow cylinder which encloses a rod of RNA. Plate VII, 2, shows virus particles in which, by chemical procedures, part of the protein has been stripped of, so that the end of the nucleic acid rod protrudes beyond its sheath. We shall come back to this picture later on.

Viruses are responsible for a host of diseases of humans, animals, plants, and even bacteria (see p. 216). They are the smallest organisms; indeed it is doubtful whether they have a right to be called organisms. One of the properties of an organism, even of a parasitic one like a tapeworm or a diphtheria bacterium, is its capacity to metabolize foodstuffs. Viruses lack this capacity. Although they can be kept alive outside the cell for long periods, especially at low temperature, they neither metabolize nor multiply under these circumstances. Nor can they be made to do so in even the most complex mixtures of nutrients, including the extracts of cells which they normally parasitize. The proper life of a virus starts only when it enters a living cell of its "host" organism. It then behaves like a prudent general who, instead of destroying agriculture and industry of an invaded territory, turns them over to his own use. A cell that has been successfully invaded by a virus uses its own enzymes for making more virus, often in large quantities. This may result in death of the cell, accompanied by a release of the newly formed virus particles, which then proceed to invade and destroy more cells. In other cases, the invading virus behaves even more prudently. It allows its host cells sufficient metabolic resources to continue their own life and multiplication while providing for life and multiplication of the invader. When this happens, the host organism, for instance a human "carrier" of a virus disease, may harbor the virus without showing outward symptoms of its presence.

A virus inside its host cell behaves very much like a gene. A gene, like a virus, cannot act or multiply outside a cell. Statements like "the gene replicates itself" and "the gene controls the production of a protein" are shorthand expressions which, written out in longhand, would read "the gene instructs the cell to make another gene like itself and to make a certain protein"; for the building blocks and the enzymes for these syntheses are all contained in the cytoplasm. In a cell that has been invaded by a virus, the instructions for making enzymes are given wholly or in part by the virus and are being used for aiding it in its replication as well as for forming certain enzymes required for this purpose.

The parallelism goes even further. The most striking fact about gene replication is its accuracy. A cell makes exact replicas of all genes that it carries; when a diploid cell contains two different allelomorphs of a particular gene, it makes faithful replicas of both. Strains of the same virus, like allelomorphs of the same gene, may show minor differences of effect; the righthand leaf in Plate VI, 2, has one bright yellow spot, which is caused by a variant form of the ordinary tobacco mosaic virus. Such variants arise suddenly like mutations, and the new type of virus particle, like a newly mutated gene, replicates accurately inside the invaded cell. Expressed in the terms used before, we may say that each variant strain of a given virus, like each mutant allele of a given gene, carries its own specific instructions into the cell.

Both the gene and the virus consist of nucleoprotein, and for both of these the question may be asked whether the specific instruction to the cell is carried in the nucleoprotein as a whole or in one of its components, either the protein or the nucleic acid. In the case of the gene, only speculations have so far been possible and these, as we saw, tended to favor the view that the protein was responsible for the specificity of the gene. In the case of the virus, experimental tests could be undertaken and these showed unequivocally that specificity is carried by the nucleic acid and not by the protein. In these tests, chemical procedures were used for separating the nucleic acid from the protein. Plate VII, 2, shows an intermediate stage in this process. The isolated nucleic acid was found to be infective for tobacco leaves, the isolated protein was not. Moreover, the nucleic acid was seen to carry the full instructions for the formation of new virus; for infection with nucleic acid from a given strain always yielded virus particles of this particular strain. Most striking of all were the results of experiments in which nucleic acid of one strain was mixed with protein of another. In such a mixture "reconstituted" virus particles are formed which carry the nucleic acid of one strain inside a sheath of protein from the other. Infection with such particles always yielded new virus that in both its protein and nucleic acid belonged to the strain that had furnished the infecting nucleic acid.

Here, then, we have a clear example of a nucleoprotein in which the nucleic acid—and only the nucleic acid—carries the specific information to the cell. Obviously, it would be rash to infer that the same must be true for the gene. Tobacco mosaic virus and genes differ in one essential point: while the nucleic acid of the gene is DNA, that of tobacco mosaic virus is RNA. In addition, while the similarities between the virus and a gene—or a collection of genes—are striking, there has as yet been no evidence that differences between strains of tobacco mosaic virus behave like differences due to mutant genes in crosses between strains; for no sexual processes have so far been discovered in tobacco mosaic virus. We shall now turn to viruses in which sexual processes do occur and which, moreover, carry DNA as their nucleic acid component.

BACTERIOPHAGE

Occasionally, a bacteriologist may find that a culture of his bacteria has "lysed," that is, that the bacteria simply have dissolved, as though they had been destroyed by something growing inside them. In the early part of this century it was discovered that this bacterial lysis is caused by viruses which multiply inside the bacteria and finally cause them to burst, liberating many new virus particles. These viruses were called "bacteriophages" (bacterium eaters); for short, they are often referred to as "phages." A simple way to demonstrate the action of phages consists in spraying them onto a surface that is completely overgrown with a lawn of susceptible bacteria. Each phage particle then invades a bacterium. When the bacterium lyses, many new particles are set free, and these in turn invade and lyse the neighboring bacteria. In the end, the bacterial lawn will be interrupted by round holes, or "plaques," each of which indicates a spot where a phage particle successfully invaded a bacterium.

Bacteriophages, like other viruses, consist of nucleoprotein, but —in contrast to tobacco mosaic virus—they have DNA as their nucleic acid component. Like tobacco mosaic virus, they have many similarities with genes. A bacterial cell that has been invaded by a bacteriophage behaves as though it had been instructed to make new phage rather than new genes. Strains of bacteriophage, like strains of tobacco mosaic virus, differ in various respects, for instance in the bacterial strains which they can invade successfully or in the size of the plaques they produce. As in tobacco mosaic virus, these differences are genetical in the sense that a new virus formed inside a bacterium is of exactly the same type as the invading particle. As in tobacco mosaic virus, strains with new properties may arise suddenly as by mutation and, once arisen, retain their new type until another mutation happens to change it.

In bacteriophage, the argument that such differences are due to mutations of true genes has been clinched by infecting bacteria with a mixture of particles from two strains. Suppose that strain A produces large clear plaques and strain B small cloudy ones, and suppose that bacteria are infected with a sufficient number of particles of both strains to ensure that many cells are invaded by both A and B particles. Then the new virus particles which are released from the lysed bacterial cells are of four types: the two original ones, forming large clear or small cloudy plaques, and two new types, forming large cloudy or small clear plaques. This recalls the result which Mendel obtained in crosses between pea plants with round yellow and wrinkled green seeds (Chap. 19). It shows that the phage particles inside their host cell go through some process of "mating," in the course of which they exchange some of their genes. Actually, the comparison with Mendel's data is not a very good one, for the genes studied by Mendel were carried on different chromosome pairs and were reassorted at meiosis, while in bacteriophages there is no meiosis and all genes are carried on the same chromosome. New combinations between genes of different phage particles are formed by a process akin to crossing over, so that a better parallel can be drawn between the four classes of phage type in the above example and the four classes of sons produced by women who are heterozygous for both hemophilia and color blindness (Chap. 20, Fig. 58). Indeed, the rules of linkage and crossing over apply so well to the genes of bacteriophage that no chromosome region in any organism has been as accurately mapped (Chap. 20, Fig. 62) as one small region in a certain strain of phage.

Phage genetics is a flourishing branch of modern genetics, and there can be no doubt that bacteriophages carry true genes, which are arranged in linear order along what may be called a phage chromosome. Are these genes formed by the nucleic acid or the protein of the phage particle?

Clean chemical separation of the phage particle into its components is not possible without loss of infectivity, but the particle itself carries out a rough kind of separation every time it infects a bacterium. Plate VII, 3, shows an electron micrograph of a bacteriophage. In its rounded shape with thin tail it somewhat resembles a tadpole. The "head" contains all the DNA in addition to a certain amount of protein; the tail consists entirely of protein. When a bacteriophage attacks a bacterium, it attaches itself to its prey by the tip of its tail (Plate VII, 4). It then makes a hole in the bacterial wall and, using its tail rather like an injection needle, injects the contents of the head into the bacterium. Although most of the injected material is nucleic acid, there is always a small admixture of protein. Nevertheless, experiments which it would take us too far to discuss have shown that the genes of a bacteriophage consist of DNA and not of protein.

In summary, then, tobacco mosaic virus and bacteriophage have each given an incomplete answer to the question: Do genes consist of nucleic acid or protein or both? In the tobacco mosaic virus it is clearly the nucleic acid, and only the nucleic acid, which carries into the host cell the specific instructions for virus reproduction; but the nucleic acid is RNA, not DNA, and the existence of separate genes has not yet been proved. The DNA of bacteriophage clearly is organized into genes which in their essential properties are like the genes of higher organisms; but the proof that these genes consist entirely of DNA is only an indirect one. Fortunately, there exists a different kind of particle which has provided an unambiguous answer at least for the genes of bacteria. This particle is called the "transforming principle," and we shall consider it in the next section; at the same time, this will allow us a glimpse into the peculiar sex life of bacteria.

THE TRANSFORMING PRINCIPLE

Pneumonia is caused by a bacterium called pneumococcus. The cells of this bacterium are oval, and each is surrounded by a capsule. When pneumococci are injected into rabbits, antibodies are produced (Chap. 10, Fig. 20). Some of these are specifically directed against the capsules, and these differ between strains of pneumococci, so that antibodies produced against the capsules of one particular strain react only with capsules of a limited number of other strains. This has led bacteriologists to group pneumococci into "types" according to their capsular antigens. Occasionally, a pneumococcus cell loses the capacity to make a capsule, and this inability is transmitted to all its progeny, so that a clone of unencapsulated cells is formed. Such clones have lost their virulence, that is, they are no longer harmful to invaded organisms. In the laboratory, they are most easily recognized by the fact that on a solid medium they form colonies which appear rough as compared with the smooth ones formed by encapsulated bacteria. It has therefore become usual to apply the terms "rough" and "smooth" to pneumococci without or with capsule.

Rough strains cannot themselves be typed because they do not produce capsular antibodies in injected animals. Rarely, however, does a bacterium in a rough strain regain the ability to form a capsule; it then gives rise to a smooth clone of the same type as the clone from which the original rough one had been derived by loss of the capsule-forming ability. Rough strains are, therefore, given the type of the smooth strain in which they originated.

In 1928 a British bacteriologist made a remarkable observation. He infected mice with a mixture of rough and heat-killed smooth bacteria, neither of which alone would have been harmful to the animals. The mixture, however, killed a high proportion of the mice. It seemed that association with the dead smooth bacteria had in some way restored the virulence of the live rough ones; indeed, when the bacteria from the dead mice were examined they were found to possess capsules and to form smooth colonies. The most surprising feature of these experiments was observed when the rough and smooth bacteria in the original mixture belonged to different types; in these cases, the rough bacteria were "transformed" into smooth ones of the type to which the killed smooth bacteria belonged. If, for instance, the rough bacteria had been derived from a Type II strain, while the killed smooth bacteria were of Type III, the rough bacteria were transformed into smooth ones of Type III. That this was not simply due to their having surrounded themselves with the capsules of the dead smooth ones followed from the fact that all their descendants were of Type III. In all similar experiments, the dead smooth bacteria transformed the rough ones into their own capsular type.

These experiments did not, at the time, receive the attention they deserved. Almost twenty years later, the work was taken up by American investigators. They found that transformation did not depend on the presence of dead bacteria, but could be equally well performed with cell-free extracts from smooth bacteria. When such extracts were further separated into their chemical components, it emerged that the whole transforming ability resided in the DNA portion, which therefore was called the "transforming principle." Once this had been established, transformation was obtained also in other species of bacteria and for other kinds of hereditary properties. Thus bacterial strains which are sensitive to antibiotics like penicillium or streptomycin, can acquire permanent resistance to these antibiotics by transformation with DNA from resistant strains.

Transformation, then, is the transmission of a heritable property from one cell to another by way of naked DNA. Various hypotheses were put forward to account for this truly amazing process. One of them suggested that the transforming principle is an isolated gene—or group of several genes—which in some way manages not only to penetrate into a living bacterial cell but also to get incorporated firmly into the genetic material of its host so that transformation may be regarded as transplantation of a gene from one individual into another. This hypothesis was later shown to be correct; but this was possible only after something had been learned about the genetic material of bacteria.

Plate VII, 5, shows bacteria after staining with one of the dyes used for staining the nuclei of higher organisms. It can be seen that every cell contains several stained bodies, which are called "nuclear bodies." In structure they are simpler than true nuclei; they are not, for instance, surrounded by a membrane like nuclei. All the same, it has been well established that they carry the genetic material of the cell.

Proof that this material consists of genes, aligned along a single chromosome, came from genetical experiments first carried out by Lederberg and Tatum, who in 1959 were awarded the Nobel Prize for their discovery of genetic recombination in bacteria. These scientists found that a mixture of bacteria with different inherited properties may give rise to strains which combine a property from one of the strains with another property from the second strain. This, as we saw in the discussion of "mating" in bacteriophages, is the essential feature of a sexual process. In bacteria, the detection of sexual processes by the appearance of new "recombinant" types can be greatly facilitated by the use of so-called screening methods. The main feature of these methods is that they kill off all bacteria except the few that, through sexual recombination, have acquired the possession of two properties that occur separately in the two parent strains. As an example we may consider two strains of intestinal bacteria, *A* and *B*. Strain *A* can grow on galactose (Chap. 24, p. 210), but is killed by streptomycin. Strain *B* is resistant to streptomycin, but cannot grow on galactose. When large numbers of both strains are spread together on medium containing streptomycin and galactose, but no other sugar, strain *A* cells will be killed by streptomycin, and strain *B* cells by starvation. The only survivors will be cells that combine the ability to grow on galactose, inherited from strain *A,* with the resistance to streptomycin, inherited from strain *B*. Many different genes have been combined with each other in experiments of this kind, and the genes of several bacterial species have been mapped in great detail.

Up to now, mating has been observed in only a few strains of bacteria. Even in those, it seemed at first to be a very rare event, but this was changed when the discovery of two sexes in bacteria made it possible to mix male and female cells in appropriate proportions. The distinction between the sexes in bacteria follows the concepts gained from higher organisms, where the female sex is the passive and the male the active partner. When bacterial cells mate, they touch each other and genetic material passes from the male into the female. So far, this process seems to fall in line with the general pattern of sexual reproduction; what makes it so original is the manner in which the male transfers its genes to the female. It appears to do so by pushing its chromosome lengthwise into the female cell at such a regular rate that it is possible to predict how many minutes after the first contact between male and female cell a given gene will pass into the female. It seems that usually the two cells move apart before the whole of the male chromosome has entered the female, for in general a mated female contains only part of the male chromosome in addition to her own. If the genes in the male chromosome differ from the corresponding ones in the female one, crossing over may lead to new combinations of genes.

Bacteria which do not mate in the described manner may use other, even more original means of exchanging genes and building up new gene combinations. Apart from the possibility that transformation of live cells by accidentally killed ones may occur in nature, many bacteria load one or a few of their genes onto phage particles, which then may carry them into a new cell where they are incorporated into the chromosome.

Investigations of all these types of sexual processes in bacteria have established the existence of bacterial genes beyond a doubt. They have also shown that transformation consists in the transfer of genes from dead into live cells and their incorporation into the host chromosome.

Since, as we saw, the transforming principle is pure DNA, the case for the bacterial genes consisting of DNA is complete. It would be unreasonable to doubt that in higher organisms, too, DNA forms an essential—probably *the* essential—part of the gene. But the role of the protein, which in the chromosomes of all higher organisms is intimately associated with DNA, remains to be explored. Meanwhile, investigations in physical chemistry have shown how eminently the structure of DNA fits it for the functions demanded from a gene. We shall consider this in the next chapter.

CHAPTER 26   *DNA*

DNA, LIKE PROTEIN, forms giant molecules which consist of smaller and simpler components. The components of protein are called "amino acids" (Chapter 23, p. 203), the components of nucleic acid are called "nucleotides." Each nucleotide, in turn, consists of three parts: a sugar molecule, a phosphate group, and a so-called purine or pyrimidine base. Purines and pyrimidines are organic molecules of a kind found in many natural products; caffeine, for instance, is a purine. All nucleotides of DNA contain the same sugar molecule, called "desoxyribose"; the nucleotides of RNA contain, instead, a sugar called "ribose," which differs from desoxyribose by having one additional oxygen atom. The bases in the different nucleotides of DNA are not all the same; there are four bases, two purines and two pyrimidines, and each nucleotide carries one of them. Rarely, a fifth base may occur.

To give the formulae of the purines and pyrimidines of DNA would take us too far into chemistry; but it will simplify the presentation of what follows if we know their chemical names. The two purines are called "adenine" (A) and "guanine" (G): the two pyrimidines are called "thymine" (T) and "cytosine" (C). Originally, it was thought that a giant molecule of DNA always contained equal numbers of A, G, T, and C; that, in fact, each such giant molecule could be subdivided into groups of four nucleotides, carrying between them just one A, one G, and one T, and one C. If this were correct, the potentialities of DNA as carrier of a genetical code would be rather limited; for—as can easily be verified—each group of four nucleotides could at best yield only 2 x 3 x 4 = 24 different "letters," and many such groups of four would be required for the spelling of even a simple "word," although thousands of "words," that is, gene-controlled processes, have to be specified for the development of even the simplest organism. Until recently, these considerations inclined most geneticists to regard the protein component of the chromosome as the essential carrier of genetic information.

This concept of the structure of DNA has now been abandoned. The proportion between the four bases in a molecule of DNA differs between species, and it is not always 1:1:1:1. There is no longer any reason to assume that the bases in a DNA molecule are arranged in groups of four; on the contrary, it is probable that they can be arranged in every possible sequence, such as AATGCGA... or TGTGCCA... and so on. This at once does away with the limitations of coding. It is evident that even very short sequences of, say, three neighboring nucleotides can "spell" large varieties of different "letters" if all possible combinations and permutations among the four bases are allowed. Three nucleotides may, for instance, spell AAA or CCC or AGA or TCA and so on. For bacteria and viruses, where DNA has been shown to carry the genetic information, it is reasonable to assume that the code is spelled by the sequence of nucleotides, and it is at least probable that this is true also for higher organisms.

There remains, however, one peculiar numerical relationship among the four bases of DNA: the number of purines is always equal to the number of pyrimidines $(A+G = T+C)$. Closer analysis shows that this matching between purines and pyrimidines goes even further, and that the number of adenines equals that of thymines $(A = T)$, while the number of guanines equals that of cytosines $(G = C)$. Thus, if in the DNA of a given species there is, for example, an excess of adenine over guanine, there is a corresponding excess of thymine over cytosine. This chemical property of DNA remained unexplained until in 1953 two young scientists at Cambridge, the Englishman Crick and the American Watson, put forward a new idea for the structure of DNA. Their model not only explained the curious quantitative relationship among the bases; it also gave a simple interpretation of one of the most puzzling biological properties of the genetic material, its ability for accurate replication. Before we consider the Watson-Crick model of DNA, let us look at the difficulties that confronted geneticists when they tried to understand gene replication.

It is difficult to think of similar processes in nature which might provide a key to the mystery. When a crystal of, say, ordinary household salt is kept in a strong solution of the same salt it "grows" by the addition of salt molecules, and the new molecules are added on in such a way that the characteristic shape of the crystal—in this particular case a cube—is maintained. The resulting large crystal can easily be split again into smaller cubes. There is a certain resemblance between gene replication and this process of growth and subdivision according to a fixed geometrical pattern, but the differences are much more striking than the similarities. A crystal has a simple molecular structure; its atoms are arranged in regular patterns. Genes—whatever their particular chemical structure—have such highly specific functions that they must differ from each other in complex and subtle ways. It is these complexities and subtleties that are replicated faithfully every time a gene multiplies, and this cannot be achieved by the simple physical forces that govern the growth of a crystal. A better comparison can be made with antibody formation. Antigens (Chapter 10) resemble genes in their high degree of specificity, and they transfer specificity to the antibodies that they provoke. The hypothesis that the procedure by which a cell makes "copies" of its genes is similar to that by which an antibody copies the specificity of the antigen is an attractive idea, but it has its difficulties. The antibody is not a copy of the antigen; their relationship to each other is that of the mold, or "template," for the stamping of a coin (Fig. 20). In order to replicate the antigen molecule itself, the antibody would have to serve as template for making an antigen, which then indeed would be exactly like the original one. Thus, theories of gene replication that are based on a comparison with antibody formation have to assume that the gene is the template for some intermediate product, which in turn is the template for the new gene. The outstanding feature of the Watson-Crick model is that it can explain gene replication without recourse to a hypothetical intermediate carrier of specificity.

Watson and Crick based their model on the X-ray diffraction picture of DNA. When X rays pass through a crystal they are scattered by its atoms, and from the pattern that the scattered beams produce on the X-ray plate an experienced scientist can infer the relative positions of the atoms to each other. This technique has been taken over for substances that are not true crystals but whose molecules, like those of protein or nucleic acid, consist of regularly arranged and spaced subunits. X-ray diffraction work on nucleic acid has been carried out for many years, mainly in London and Cambridge. In 1953 Watson and Crick suggested a new interpretation of these data, which is shown diagrammatically

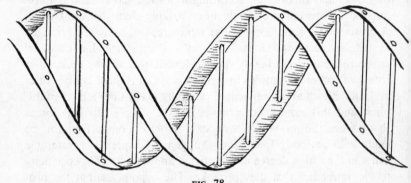

FIG. 78.
The strucure of DNA according to Watson and Crick.

in Fig. 78. The DNA molecule, only part of which is shown, consists of two threads that are wound spirally round each other. Since the diameter of the windings remains the same throughout the molecule, it is more correct to speak of helical winding and to call the whole structure a double helix. In reality, of course, the strands are not solid fibers but consist of individual atoms, held together by strong chemical bonds. Weaker bonds connect the two strands crosswise and hold them together. Chemically, the strands are formed by alternating units of phosphate and sugar; the bases are attached to the sugar, one base to each sugar unit, and they reach out into the hollow cylinder formed by the two winding strands. Opposite bases are held together by weak chemical bonds. If we imagine the strands unwound and the whole structure flattened out it would look somewhat like this:

Now, of the two kinds of base, the purines are considerably larger than the pyrimidines. If a pyrimidine on one strand were paired with a pyrimidine on the other, the diameter of the whole structure in this region would be narrower than in a region where two purines were paired. If one wants to preserve the same width throughout the whole DNA molecule, one has to arrange the bases in such a way that at every crosslink a purine is paired with a pyrimidine. Since, as the X-ray diffraction picture shows, the diameter of DNA does not change from region to region, this must be the way the bases are arranged in nature. You will realize that this conclusion automatically results in equal proportions of purines and pyrimidines and explains one of the hitherto puzzling numerical relations among the bases. Moreover, when the chemical configurations of the individual bases are taken into account it turns out that, in order to fit into the available space, adenine has to pair with thymine, and guanine with cytosine. This explains why there are always as many adenines as thymines and as many guanines as cytosines in a molecule of DNA. The base sequences in the two strands are thus complementary to each other: if we choose one of them arbitrarily, the other one is no longer open to choice. If, for instance, the sequence in a region of one strand is . . . AGGTTCTGAC . . . then the opposite sequence necessarily is . . . TCCAAGACTG. . . .

It remains to discuss the greatest attraction of the Watson-Crick model for the geneticist: its ability to provide a simple mechanism for gene replication. According to present-day theory, DNA duplicates itself in the following way: First, the two strands unwind and separate; how this is achieved is still somewhat of a puzzle. Once the strands are free, the base sequences, which according to our present view carry the genetical code, are exposed to the surrounding fluid, which contains all kinds of chemical building blocks, among them phosphate, sugar, and the four purine and pyrimidine bases required for synthesis of DNA. From this store of building material each base of an original strand attaches to itself a new base, and these new bases then become linked with each other by a new sugar-phosphate strand, which proceeds to wind round the old one and form a double helix with it. The most important point about the whole process is that the old bases are not free in the choice of the new ones. Unless each base chooses its complementary one, that is, unless A chooses T, T chooses A, G chooses C, and C chooses G, there will be a bulge or a constriction in the new double helix wherever such a wrong choice has been made, and this poor fit will cause the unsuited base to be replaced by the fitting one. The whole process may be illustrated in the following diagram, where the new bases and strands are shown bold face.

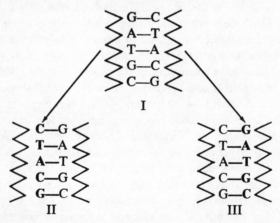

This diagram shows the essential features of DNA replication, as envisaged by modern theory: each "daughter" chromosome is made up of one old and one new strand, and the specific base sequence in the two daughter molecules (II and III) is the same as in the original one (I).

Like every major discovery, the Watson-Crick model has posed many more questions than it has answered, questions such as: Is the whole of the chromosomal DNA used for coding, or does a chromosome contain some "nonsense" sequences, which are used as full stops or commas or for some altogether different purpose? Is the genetical information restricted to DNA, even in higher organisms in which the chromosomal DNA is always tightly bound up with protein and a certain amount of RNA? How is the code deciphered and translated into specific biochemical processes? RNA obviously plays a major role in this; but how exactly does it function?

With these questions we have reached the very frontiers of present-day research. To deal further with them would be beyond the scope of this book. We shall, however, see in the next chapter how the discovery of Crick and Watson has influenced our attempts to find answers to the old questions: what are mutations, and how do they arise?

CHAPTER 27 *Mutation*

WE SPEAK OF MUTATION when a new Mendelian character appears in a strain of organisms that previously had been free of it. The Ancon character in sheep and the platinum character in mink (Chap. 7) arose by mutation in strains of domesticated animals. Queen Victoria came from a family in which hemophilia had not been known until it appeared in one of her sons and, subsequently, in several sons of her daughters (Chap. 15); apparently a mutation to hemophilia had occurred in a germ cell of one of her parents, so that she herself was already heterozygous for the newly mutated gene.

An observed mutation reflects a change in a gene. Presumably the mutated gene differs from the original one in chemical composition or structure. The new gene, like the old one, must be capable of accurate self-replication, for a mutated gene replicates in the mutated form. There is no recovery from mutation except in the very rare cases when a subsequent mutation restores the original gene. If our present view of the nature of the gene is correct, a mutation consists in a change in the number, types, or arrangement of nucleotides that "spell" a gene. On the Watson-Crick model of DNA replication, such changes would be perpetuated.

Mutation is not restricted to the germ cells; however, in sexually reproducing species only mutations that occur in germ cells are transmitted to the progeny. In asexually propagated species, mutations that occur in ordinary body cells may become established as mutant strains: many varieties of fruit trees have originated as "bud sports." In a diploid species, recessive mutations can produce bud sports or mosaics only when the individual is already heterozygous for the gene in question. Plate VIII, 1, shows a snapdragon flower which is half purple and half lavender; it grew on a branch which, in addition to two or more such mosaic flowers, also bore several that were either wholly purple or wholly lavender. The plant itself was heterozygous for the recessive lavender gene, and in one of the cells from which the mosaic branch developed the normal allele had mutated to lavender. Dominant mutations may give rise to immediately observable bud sports or mosaics.

Mutation takes place regularly in all species of organisms. Each individual gene mutates only very rarely, perhaps once in 100,000 or once in a million cells; but as the number of genes in most organisms is very high the over-all mutation frequency per generation may be considerable. In man some mutations, for instance, that to hemophilia, occur at the relatively high frequency of about one in 50,000; this means that about one out of 50,000 gametes carries a newly arisen gene for hemophilia. For various reasons, it is likely that the majority of human genes mutate less frequently, perhaps once in 100,000 gametes or even more rarely. If we make the conservative assumption that the 23 chromosomes in a human gamete between them carry 10,000 genes, then it would follow that one gamete out of ten carries a newly mutated gene. This is not more than a rough guess, but it is not likely to be too high.

Only a small fraction of new mutations is immediately detectable as mutant offspring. A recessive mutation in the gamete of a diploid species will yield phenotypically normal offspring, unless the other gamete happens to carry the same recessive gene as the result of a previous mutation in the population. Apart from such cases, a newly arisen recessive gene may be carried in heterozygotes for many generations, until the mating of two such heterozygotes produces a homozygous offspring. An exception is formed by sex-linked recessive mutations (Chap. 15); these will show up in the first XY individual with the mutated gene. Even dominant or partially dominant mutations do not always give rise to detectably mutant progeny. Many of them produce effects that are too small to be observed or that might equally well be attributed to environmental influences. This applies particularly to mutations affecting quantitative characters (Chap. 21), for instance, egg production in poultry, grain yield in corn, general vigor, or intelligence. Thus the realization that about one out of ten human gametes carries a new mutation does not mean that about one out of ten children will be in some way abnormal or unusual. It does, however, mean that in man, as in every other species, new mutations occur inexorably even without artificial causes such as exposure to X rays.

These new mutations must not be thought of as new in the sense that they have not occurred before. A species has a limited number of genes, and each gene can mutate only to a limited number of alleles. Each mutation of a given gene to a given allele recurs at a certain low frequency, and in a species with a long evolutionary history every possible mutation is likely to have occurred repeatedly. In microorganisms, in which millions of cells can be screened for mutations, it is easy to see that the same mutations turn up again and again.

This is an important fact. It explains why the majority of mutations are harmful. In a species that, through long periods of evolution, has become adapted to its mode of life all useful alleles that can arise by mutation will already have been incorporated into the genotype, so that all or most members of the species carry them in homozygous condition (Chap. 29). Once this stage has been reached, only harmful or at least less valuable alleles can still occur as new mutations. Most desert animals have a yellow-gray coat color, which forms an effective camouflage. Evolution in the desert has favored animals with the right type of coat-color genes, and alleles arising from new mutations can only be to lighter or darker shades, away from the best possible one. This is a simple example, but the same principle applies to more complicated cases in which many genes interact to produce the best-adapted phenotype. Indeed, the more complex the genetic control of a character the more readily is it upset by mutation in one of its controlling genes. A primitive piece of machinery may continue to work when one of its pieces has been replaced by a slightly different one; a complicated apparatus will be wrecked by the slightest alteration in the dimensions or position of one of its cogs or levers. Yet even the most complicated man-made machine is simple compared with the most primitive living organism.

The fact that the majority of mutations is harmful has recently developed into a matter of immediate and grave concern. As long as mutations occur only from natural sources, there is nothing we can do about controlling their frequency. Modern man, however, is making use of agents that artificially increase the frequency of mutations above its natural level. Foremost among these agents are high-energy radiations from X-ray machines, from fallout produced by nuclear tests, and from a number of other sources. The benefits to be derived from these devices have to be balanced against the harm we inflict on unborn generations by loading them with an increased burden of mutated genes. So much has been written about this urgent and difficult problem that it would be redundant to discuss it here. Only one point may be mentioned. The question is often raised whether new mutations may not sometimes be beneficial. This is, indeed, true. Very occasionally beneficial mutations occur. Plant breeders have successfully used radiation or chemical treatment for obtaining useful mutations in cereals, ornamental plants, fruit trees, and other plants. Irradiation of molds like Penicillium has produced strains with increased yield of antibiotic. But each such useful mutation has been obtained at the cost of about a thousand harmful or useless ones, which had to be discarded. Even in animal breeding such a procedure would be impossibly wasteful. For mankind any increase in mutation frequency remains highly undesirable in spite of the possibility that among a thousand harmful mutations there may be one that is beneficial.

While the genetical dangers of radiation are among the most widely discussed topics of our time, much less attention is paid to the possibility that mutations may be produced by some of the many chemicals that civilized man uses in his food, his drugs, his cosmetics, his industrial processes. There is a good reason for the lack of scientific pronouncement on this question: our profound ignorance of the relevant facts. It is true that the past twenty years have seen the discovery of an ever-increasing number of chemicals that produce mutations in Drosophila, in plants, and in microorganisms. But while it may be confidently assumed that human genes, like those of every other tested species including mice, will mutate on exposure to ionizing radiation, the same cannot be taken for granted in regard to chemical "mutagens." X rays penetrate easily through living matter of every description. Chemicals may be retained by the outer layers of the body before they reach the germ cells; they may be excreted before they have had a chance to produce mutations; they may be trapped by cell constituents outside the nucleus; they may be metabolized into compounds with different chemical properties. All these possibilities will differ between species, and a chemical that produces many mutations in one organism may be quite ineffective in another. Thus caffeine has produced mutations in certain bacteria and fungi. In Drosophila it has had a similar, but much weaker, effect. Its effect on the germ cells of mice, rats or guinea pigs remains to be tested by experiment. Whether it is a mutagen for people who imbibe it in coffee or tea cannot be decided experimentally. Data on mice and other laboratory mammals can provide no more than presumptive evidence, which different geneticists will interpret differently according to their scientific caution and their degree of addiction to coffee or tea. Yet, to obtain such data remains an urgent object for genetical research in the near future.

Mutation research thus forms an important branch of applied genetics, both positively, as a tool for the production of improved strains of plants and microorganisms, and negatively, as a means for detecting possible harmful genetical effects of processes and chemicals used in human societies. For the research worker mutation work is one of the most valuable tools in the study of the genetic material. When in 1927, at the Fifth International Congress of Genetics in Berlin, H. J. Muller from the United States first reported the production of mutations in Drosophila by X rays he opened a new chapter in the history of genetics. With the aid of X-ray machines, every laboratory worker could now produce unprecedented numbers of new mutations in whatever organism he was studying. These mutations, in turn, provided material for all types of genetical investigation, which without this might have had to wait for decades until the right kind of mutation turned up spontaneously. Nowadays the geneticist who wants some particular mutation for his experiments turns quite naturally to the X-ray machine to provide it.

In research on microorganisms, ultraviolet radiation serves the same purpose more effectively. Most of the mutations for the study of gene action in microorganisms (Chapter 23) or of genetic recombination in bacteria (Chapter 25) were produced by exposure of cells to ultraviolet light. In higher organisms, too, ultraviolet light can produce mutations when it reaches the nucleus of the germ cells; but shielding through the outer layers of tissue is so great that special tricks have to be used to ensure penetration. Although excessive exposure of the human body to the ultraviolet light of the sun may cause nasty burns, we need not worry about its effect on the progeny.

The first chemicals with mutagenic action were discovered at the beginning of the Second World War. At present we know scores of such substances, belonging to very different chemical groups. Some, like mustard gas and certain related substances, have produced mutations in every kind of tested organism. Others act only on certain types of organism or cell. Formaldehyde, for instance, produces mutations in Drosophila males but not in Drosophila females. In recent years much effort has been directed toward finding chemicals that are even more selective and act only on certain genes. Obviously the detection of such substances would be of tremendous importance for the theory and practice of genetics. For the research worker they would provide a tool for studying the chemical nature of individual genes; for the applied geneticist they would provide means for producing at will mutations of a desirable type. We are still far from having reached this goal, but there have been encouraging signs that it may not be unattainable. It is already clear that chemicals may differ from radiation and from each other in the relative frequencies with which they produce different mutations.

We still know little about the manner in which radiation or chemical mutagens produce their effects. X rays and similar types of radiation release large amounts of energy on their passage through living matter; when this happens in or near a chromosome it may result in chemical change of a gene. The much smaller amounts of energy released by ultraviolet radiation may act in a similar way; but possibly much of the mutagenic action of ultraviolet light is mediated by chemical effects of the radiation on the fluid surrounding the genes. To some extent this appears to be true even for high-energy radiations like X rays. Mutagenic chemicals may react with the genes directly, or indirectly through reactions with the cytoplasm. It is also possible—and indeed may be a frequent cause of mutation—that a gene "makes a mistake" when it replicates. One can imagine many ways by which a mutagen may provoke such mistakes. Especially mutagens that are chemically related to the purines and pyrimidines in DNA are liable to act in this way.

Our ideas about what causes mutations to occur in nature are even more speculative. Certainly radiation from cosmic rays and from radioactive substances in the soil and the organisms themselves must contribute their share of mutations; but the amount of radiation from these sources is too low to account for more than a small part of all naturally occurring mutations. Mutagenic chemicals may be responsible for much or all of the remainder. Several known mutagens are natural products; quite recently, a very potent mutagen—heliotrin—has been found in the common ragwort. In bacteria, at least, a proportion of naturally occurring mutations seems to be due to mutagenic purines that are produced in the cells themselves. This can be concluded from experiments in which purines such as caffeine or related substances were used for producing mutations. The mutagenic effect of the purines could be completely prevented when the bacteria were given certain other substances, which in some way acted as "antimutagens." When untreated bacteria were grown in solutions of these antimutagens they developed many fewer mutations than bacteria grown in ordinary nutrient solution. As would be expected, the antimutagens did not interfere with the production of mutations by radiation.

After these speculations we reach firm ground again when we consider a different kind of genetical change which occurs infrequently in nature and can be induced by radiation and many chemicals: chromosome breakage. In organisms with sufficiently large chromosomes it is easy to see breakage by X rays, mustard gas, or other mutagenic treatment; in other organisms breakage may be detected by genetical methods, that is, by examination of the progeny. The genetical consequences of chromosome breakage depend on the fate of the broken chromosomes. In some way which is not yet fully understood broken chromosome ends can stick together to form again permanent structures; but, as chromosomes in a living cell float freely in the nuclear sap, the new chromosomes are not always the same as the original ones. Chromosomes may exchange pieces, fragments may be lost, and other kinds of "structural change" may take place. In the present context the most important change is a "deficiency," that is, loss of a fragment either from the end of a chromosome or, through rejoining between the wrong pieces (Fig. 79), from one of its inner regions. A fragment that fails to rejoin usually is lost, and with it the genes carried on it. In a haploid organism like Chlamydomonas or many strains of yeast and other fungi all but the smallest deficiencies result in death, for, as was stressed in Chapter 23, the vast majority of genes are necessary for survival. Two examples of deficiencies in diploid organisms have been discussed in Chapter 4 and are illustrated in Figs. 3 and 4. Either deficiency kills homozygotes, that is, individuals lacking the same gene or genes in both partner chromosome; but, while the deficiency shown in Fig. 4 has no noticeable

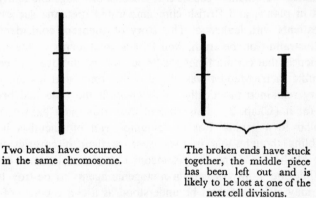

Two breaks have occurred in the same chromosome.

The broken ends have stuck together, the middle piece has been left out and is likely to be lost at one of the next cell divisions.

FIG. 79.
Origin of a chromosome deficiency.

effect on the heterozygote, the deficiency shown in Fig. 3 makes even the heterozygote strikingly abnormal. Thus the first deficiency behaves like a recessive gene, the second like a dominant one.

Cells with broken chromosomes, whether or not these rejoin into rearrangements, survive well as long as they do not divide, but for various reasons they usually die at the next division or soon after. This explains why dividing cells are much more sensitive to radiation than nondividing ones. The selective killing of dividing cells by X rays is utilized in the treatment of cancer. Tumors characteristically contain a much higher proportion of dividing cells than the surrounding normal tissue and are therefore selectively destroyed by radiation.

Treatment with mutagenic chemicals is of more recent origin. These chemicals, like X rays, destroy tumor cells by chromosome breakage; they may give good results especially in cases where X rays cannot be used. The first chemical of this kind was nitrogen mustard. Its value for the treatment of cancer was discovered in the United States at the beginning of the Second World War. Simultaneously and independently the first chemically induced mutations in Drosophila were found in Scotland in the progeny of flies that had been exposed to mustard gas or nitrogen mustard. Also at the same time, and without knowledge of the American and British work, German scientists found that an entirely different substance—urethane—causes chromosome breakage and rearrangement in plants, and British clinicians tested urethane successfully on patients with leukemia. This story of apparent coincidences is an illustration of the truth, well known to students of the history of science, that certain times are "ripe" for the discovery of certain scientific facts. Mendel was ahead of his time, and his great discovery remained practically unknown until the time had become ripe for it (Chap. 2). This kind of misfortune is a hazard that is peculiar to a genius. For the common run of scientists it is a humbling thought that in their absence their discoveries would probably have been made by someone else within the same decade.

While the ability of certain mutagenic agents to destroy tumor cells may at least in part be understood as a consequence of their ability to break chromosomes, another connection between mutagenesis and cancer is less easily interpreted. It is well known that X rays not only can *cure* cancer but that continued exposure to low doses of X rays may *produce* cancer, as the early X-ray workers learned to their great detriment. The same parallelism has meanwhile been found for a number of chemical mutagens, including nitrogen mustard and urethane. One school of scientists regards these findings as support for the theory that for certain types of malignant growth the primary cause is a mutation by which a cell escapes the growth control imposed by the organism and starts on a course of unchecked divisions. These scientists are aware of the fact that tumor cells differ from normal ones in their metabolism, but they attribute this to secondary consequences of the original mutation. Other scientists are more impressed by these metabolic disturbances and look for changes in the cytoplasm as the primary cause of cancer. Since all the cells in a tumor can be considered as a clone (Chap. 5) descended from one original abnormal cell, this theory advocates the origin of an inherited change by some kind of cytoplasmic mutation; it challenges the monopoly of the genes in determining hereditary characteristics. This is a problem of wider scope than theories concerning the origin of cancer; we shall discuss it further in the next chapter.

CHAPTER 28   *The Monopoly of the Genes in Inheritance*

══

SO FAR, we have considered only cases in which the transmission of a character depends on genes, although its manifestation may be influenced by environment. Since the genes are in the nucleus, this type of inheritance is called "nuclear." The overwhelming majority of well-studied cases of inheritance are nuclear, but this does not mean that "extranuclear" or "cytoplasmic" inheritance is impossible. In fact, we have already encountered one case of extranuclear inheritance in Chapter 23. Chlorophyll formation, as we saw, is under the control of a large number of genes; but these genes require the co-operation of the chloroplast. Changes may occur in a chloroplast that make it unable to respond to the controlling genes, and these changes may be transmitted from the first abnormal chloroplast to all its descendants. Many cases of chloroplast inheritance are known, and since chloroplasts—like genes—reproduce by replication and division, this type of extranuclear inheritance is fairly well understood.

Other cases of cytoplasmic inheritance exist and can be detected by special methods. Two rules are used for their detection, one negative, one positive. The negative rule states that hereditary traits which are transmitted through the cytoplasm must not show Mendelian segregation in crosses. The positive rule is based on the fact that, at least in all higher organisms, the female gamete contains a large amount of cytoplasm, while the male gamete contains very little. One would therefore expect that cytoplasmically inherited characters would follow the maternal line. This is, indeed, true for chloroplast inheritance. In a cross between plants with normal and abnormal chloroplasts, *all* the progeny have normal chloroplasts if those of the mother plant were normal and abnormal ones if those of the mother plant were abnormal. Occasionally, some chloroplasts may be transmitted through the pollen, but this does not alter the essential difference between the progeny of the two "reciprocal" crosses.

A comparison between the results of reciprocal crosses is the most useful tool in the search for cytoplasmic inheritance. But it is a tool that has to be used with caution, for differences between progenies of reciprocal matings may occur also when inheritance is purely nuclear. The simplest example is sex-linked inheritance (Chap. 15). A cross between a gold cock ss and a silver hen S produces silver cockerels Ss and gold pullets s (Fig. 40); the reciprocal cross between a silver cock SS and a gold hen s produces only silver offspring: the cockerels are $Ss,$ the pullets are S. Such cases are easily distinguished from cytoplasmic inheritance.

Another cause for differences between reciprocal crosses is early gene action in the unfertilized ovum. Figure 80 illustrates one such case. In the flour moth Ephestia, the normal black eye color of the caterpillars and moths develops through a series of biochemical steps (Chap. 23, Figs. 74–75), one of which is blocked when a gene A is replaced by its allelomorph a. A is dominant over $a,$ and the eyes of Aa caterpillars and moths are black like those of homozygotes AA. The eyes of aa animals are light because one of the necessary precursor substances is not produced in the absence of A. When a heterozygous black-eyed male Aa is crossed with a light-eyed female aa (Fig. 80, I), the progeny segregates into 50 per cent Aa caterpillars with black eyes and 50 per cent aa caterpillars with light eyes, just as could have been predicted from Mendel's first law (Fig. 13). The reciprocal cross (Fig. 80, II) gives a different result. Here all caterpillars have black eyes. That segregation into Aa and aa did, nevertheless, occur can be seen when the moths emerge from their cocoons; for half of them have black eyes and half have white eyes, exactly as in cross I. Apparently the A gene in the mother produces sufficient precursor substance in the egg to last through the lifetime of the caterpillar; when the store is exhausted, no more can be formed in the absence of gene *A*, and no black eye pigment develops in the moth. Again it is clear that we are dealing with nuclear and not with cytoplasmic inheritance. The distinction would have been less easy if the effect of the maternal gene had persisted throughout the life of the progeny. This, too, may happen and gives rise to cases that at first sight look like cytoplasmic inheritance.

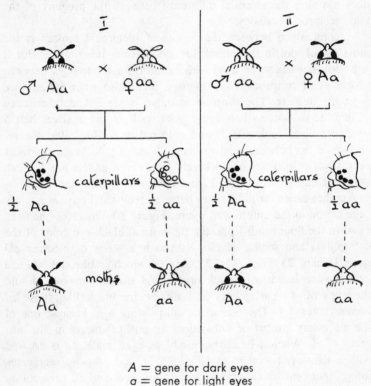

A = gene for dark eyes
a = gene for light eyes

FIG. 80.
Maternal inheritance in the flour moth Ephestia.

Figure 81, II, shows the two types of coiling that occur in shells of the pond snail Limnaea. Whether an individual will develop a left-handed or a right-handed coil depends on the arrangement of the first four cells in the young embryo (Fig. 81, I), and this in turn depends on a pattern of asymmetry that is laid down in the unfertilized egg under the influence of the mother's genes. One pair of genes controls this pattern, *D* the gene for right-handed coiling being dominant over its recessive allele *d* for left-handed coiling. A mother of genotype *DD* or *Dd* has only right-handed offspring, independent of the genotype of the father. Similarly, a mother of genotype *dd* has only left-handed offspring. In general, the direction of coiling in any individual is determined by the genotype of its mother, not by its own genotype. This can easily be followed in the breeding scheme illustrated in Fig. 82, in which use has been made of the fact that snails are hermaphroditic, that is, they have both male and female sex organs and are capable of

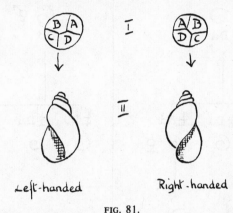

FIG. 81.

Right-handed and left-handed coiling of the shell in the pond snail Limnaea. I. The first four cells of the developing embryo. II. The finished shell.

either self-fertilization or cross-fertilization. If the breeding tests had not been continued beyond the first generation, this would have seemed a clear case of cytoplasmic inheritance according to our rules; for there was no segregation, and in reciprocal crosses all offspring had the maternal phenotype.

When all similar instances of "maternal inheritance" of nuclear effects are left aside, there remain a number of cases that must be attributed to cytoplasmic inheritance, or at least to inheritance by way of the cytoplasm. This is not a purely verbal distinction; it refers to the experience that several cases of what appeared to be cytoplasmic inheritance turned out to be transmission of a micro-organism through the cytoplasm. Perhaps the most spectacular case is that of the "killers" and "mate-killers" in the tiny fresh-water animal Paramecium (Fig. 83). This organism consists of one cell and produces clones by continued division into two; in addition,

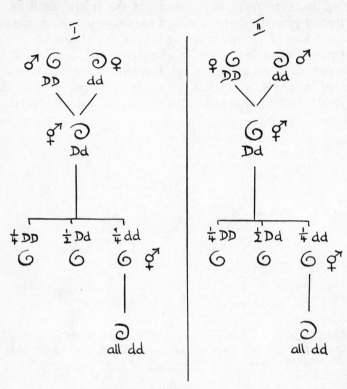

6 = shell with right-hand coil
∂ = shell with left-hand coil
d = recessive allele for left-handed coiling
♂ = animal used as male in a cross
♀ = animal used as female in a cross
♂ = animal self-fertilized

FIG. 82.
Maternal inheritance in Limnaea.

mating occurs and gives Mendelian segregation of genes. When different clones of this animal are kept together in a container, it may happen that all those of one clone are killed by a secretion from the other. For the killers themselves, this secretion is harmless. Different killer strains have different means of killing their victims. Most of them do not kill their mates; but there are some strains that, instead of killing from a distance by secretion, kill their mates through close contact. The killer character has a nuclear as well as a cytoplasmic basis. The situation is very similar for ordinary killers and mate-killers; it will be described for the former. The nuclear basis is a pair of alleles K and k. Animals that are homozygous for k are sensitive to killing and cannot themselves become killers. Animals that carry the K homozygously or heterozygously in normal cytoplasm are potential killers; they are actual killers when their cytoplasm contains particles called "kappa," which in turn produce the lethal poison. In KK or Kk animals kappa particles are transmitted from cell to cell in the

FIG. 83.

The microscopic animal Paramecium (sometimes called the slipper animalcule because of its shape). The large bean-shaped body and the small round one adjoining it are nuclei. The star-shaped structures are vacuoles which pump superfluous fluid out of the cell.

cytoplasm; once they have been lost from a cell they do not again develop by themselves. The inheritance of kappa was at first considered a good example of cytoplasmic inheritance. Closer studies, however, showed that the kappa particles resemble bacteria, and their transmission from cell to cell in the cytoplasm is therefore more aptly compared with the transmission of a parasitic microorganism. The fact that kappa particles can be maintained only in animals with the gene K is no argument against this interpretation. It is a very common observation that resistance or sensitivity to a parasite may depend on the genotype of the infected host. In man there is evidence for genetically determined sensitivity to the polio virus (Chap. 16), and bacterial strains may become resistant to a bacteriophage (Chap. 25) through mutation of one of their genes.

In Drosophila, certain animals are hypersensitive to the effects of carbon dioxide and are killed by doses that have only slight and transitory effects on normal flies. This property is inherited cytoplasmically; but, again, the responsible particles appears to be a virus rather than a normal component of cytoplasm. A decision between these alternatives is not easy, and geneticists are divided in their interpretation of this case and similar ones. But even if all of them are attributed to true cytoplasmic inheritance, their number among animals is exceedingly small and is not likely to be increased considerably by future discoveries. It is somewhat larger in plants, where reciprocal crosses often differ and the differences do not always regard the chloroplasts. One character that in many plants is inherited through the cytoplasm has a certain economic importance. This is male sterility, the inability to form functional pollen. Where, as in the breeding of hybrid corn, self-fertilization has to be prevented, the introduction of the cytoplasmic factor for male sterility into the line used as female parent can save much work.

In summary, it seems safe to conclude that in the control of inheritance the monopoly of the genes, although not absolute, is very strong. Whether cytoplasmic inheritance plays a role in determining differences between widely differing organisms, belonging to different species or genera, is a much-debated question. Unfortunately, it is not amenable to experimental solution, because crosses between species or genera are usually sterile or, if fertile, have sterile progeny (like the mule). We shall not consider cytoplasmic inheritance when, in the next and last chapter, we shall throw a brief glance at the forces that have brought about evolution.

CHAPTER 29   *Evolution as Seen
by the Geneticist*

EVOLUTION IS A historical fact. Its truth is as well established as a historical truth ever can be established. Evidence for it is provided by many branches of biology; for instance, the study of fossils, of comparative anatomy, of the geographical distribution of animals and plants. Genetics is not concerned with providing evidence for the fact that evolution has occurred, but with explaining, how it occurred. The geneticist's picture of evolution has been described in many modern books, some of them written for the nonbiologist; here we can do no more than sketch its barest outline.

Darwin explained evolution as the consequence of natural selection acting on naturally occurring variants. These variants arise by chance and may be of all kinds; natural selection is the directing force that channels them into the path of evolutionary progress. The principles of natural selection have already been discussed briefly in Chapter 13. We may restate it here in the following way: Among the naturally occurring variants in any population, those that are best adapted to the present way of life of the organism leave more progeny than the remainder. If the traits that made the parents "fitter" than the average are inherited, they will reappear in their descendants, where they will again result in increased fitness, that is, in a more than average number of offspring. In the end, well-adapted individuals will replace the less well-adapted ones, and the whole population will fit snugly into the "niche" of its special environment.

When these ideas were first put forward in Darwin's book *Origin of Species* (1859), they were hailed with enthusiasm, and for decades biological thought was dominated by them. The criticism that followed centered mainly round the problem of natural variability. According to Darwin, naturally occurring variants form the material on which natural selection acts, and questions were raised as to the suitability of this material for its purpose. Do enough variants arise in every generation? Are they of the right types? Finally, and perhaps most important, are the variant traits transmitted to the progeny? If they are not, they are useless for selection for, as we saw in Chapter 21, selection for phenotypical characters without a genetical basis is entirely ineffective. There were important additional questions. But before mentioning some of them let us try to find answers to those relating to genetic variations in nature; for it is with these answers that Darwin's theory of evolution must stand or fall.

The ultimate source of genetic variability is mutation. Mutation, as we saw in Chapter 27, is a process that occurs regularly in nature. It is a rare process; a given gene may mutate, say, once in a million cells or even as rarely as once in a hundred million cells. But a bacterium that divides into two every two hours can form a clone of a hundred million cells in less than three days, and the male organs of most higher organisms produce millions of spermatozoa or pollen grains. In addition, evolution has been going on for many million of years. Thus there has been no lack of opportunity for every possible mutation to have occurred repeatedly.

Yet, if the achievements of evolution are compared with its time scale, it appears that mutation alone would hardly have been sufficient to provide all the required genetic variation except in such rapidly reproducing organisms as bacteria. In higher organisms the number of mutant individuals that are produced within a certain time span has been severely restricted by two factors: the longer interval between generations and the smaller number of offspring. These species still have to rely on mutations as their ultimate raw material; but they use them as an architect may use building blocks of different sizes, shapes and colors for making many different kinds of patterns. In these species the main source of genetic variation is recombination according to Mendel's second law (Chap. 19) or, for linked genes, by crossing over (Chap. 20). While the animal breeder may find it difficult or impossible to separate or combine two closely linked genes (Chap. 20), evolution has so much time at its disposal that even very close linkage is no serious obstacle to recombination.

The amount of genetic variability that results from recombination is tremendous. Let us consider four of the gene pairs with which Mendel worked: (1) round seed versus wrinkled seed (Chap. 6); (2) yellow seed versus green seed (Chap. 19); (3) tall plant versus short plant; (4) red flower versus white flower. We have already seen (Chap. 19) that recombination between the first two gene pairs results in four phenotypical classes: round yellow, round green, wrinkled yellow, wrinkled green. Within each class recombination with the third pair will result in subdivision into tall and short plants, so that altogether there will now be $2 \times 2 \times 2 = 8$ different classes. Recombination with the fourth gene pair will again subdivide each class into two, so that recombination for all four gene pairs yields $2 \times 2 \times 2 \times 2 = 16$ classes. So it will go on, each new pair of alleles doubling the number of phenotypical classes. Most species carry thousands or tens of thousands of genes, and a large proportion of these occur as two or more alleles. Let us make the assumption—which certainly is a gross underestimate—that in the human species there are only 100 genes that occur as different alleles, and that for each of these genes there are only two alternative alleles, one of which is recessive. Then the number of possible phenotypes that can arise through recombination between these 100 allele pairs is $2 \times 2 \times 2 \ldots$ one hundred times. When the calculation is carried through, it yields a figure that consists of a 1 followed by 30 zeros; expressed in words, this figure reads a million million million million millions. The number of genotypes is very much larger; for each pair of alleles A, a gives rise to *three* classes of genotype AA, Aa, and aa, which in cases of incomplete dominance (Fig. 12) are phenotypically distinct. Recombination between 100 pairs of alleles thus yields $3 \times 3 \times 3 \ldots$ one hundred times, and this works out as a 1 with 50 zeros. Since the whole human population on earth is less than 3,000 million, that is, less than 3 billion individuals, it is obvious that there is practically no chance for two individuals—excepting identical twins—to be genetically alike.

The enormous importance of recombination for evolution can be seen from the fact that some kind of sexual mechanism, allowing recombination of genes, has evolved in all groups of organism, down to bacteria and viruses (Chap. 25). Sex, like many steps in the progression of life on earth, is both a result and a cause of evolution.

Having satisfied ourselves that there exists in nature an abundance of genetic variability, we may ask whether the variants are of the right type to serve as material for evolution. This has been doubted for a variety of reasons, the most important of which may be stated as follows: (1) Mutations are harmful and cannot explain progress in evolution. (2) Mutations are large deviations from the norm, while evolution—according to Darwin—proceeds gradually. (3) Mutations affect only superficial characters, such as eye color, while species differ from each other in fundamental traits of their anatomy or physiology. These statements were based on the early findings of genetical research at the beginning of this century and are now obsolete. We shall consider them in turn.

1. We have already seen (Chap. 27) that most mutations are indeed harmful when they occur in a species that—through previous mutation, recombination, and selection—is already well adapted to its mode of life. This, rather than being an argument against natural selection, is evidence for its efficacy in the past. But during the long periods of evolutionary time conditions are bound to change for every species, and when this happens mutations that previously would have been harmful may become beneficial; they may, indeed, save the species from extinction. It is the great advantage of diploidy (Chap. 3) that it permits potentially useful recessive genes to be carried in heterozygotes until the time when they can prove their value.

Darwin explained the prevalence of species with rudimentary or no wings among insects inhabiting islands or windy coasts by assuming that under these environmental conditions wings would be disadvantageous and wingless mutants would be selected. French biologists carried out an experiment to test this hypothesis. In Drosophila, a recessive gene "vestigial" changes the wings into tiny rudiments. Vestigial flies cannot fly and are at a severe disadvantage in the normal environment of wild Drosophila species. A mixture of long-winged and vestigial flies was released in a windy region on the coast of France. The flies with long wings were carried away by the wind much more readily than the vestigial ones, and the proportion of vestigial flies in the released population increased rapidly. If a wild population of Drosophila were forced to live under similar conditions, the previously harmful mutation vestigial might acquire selective value.

2. The belief that most mutations have drastic effects has its roots in the history of genetics. The scientist who introduced the term "mutation"—one of the three rediscoverers of Mendel in 1900 (Chap. 2)—applied it to striking hereditary changes which he had observed in the evening primrose and most of which were, in fact, not mutations but unusual types of recombinations. Subsequently, geneticists during the early years of this century chose striking mutants for establishing the fundamental rules of inheritance. This choice was dictated by common sense; if Mendel had weighed each pea in order to follow the inheritance of small differences in weight, he would never have found his rules. In actual fact, mutations with small effect are very common; anybody who looks for them is sure to find them, but the work is laborious and tedious. Obviously, therefore, more large than small mutations will be *detected;* but doubtless the true frequency of the latter is much higher than that of the former.

Two kinds of small mutation have been of special significance in evolution. The first are mutations affecting quantitative characters like body size or fertility; for, as we saw in Chapter 21, such characters are controlled by the cumulative action of many genes with individually small effects. The second are mutations in so-called modifying genes. These are genes that do not by themselves produce noticeable effects, but modify the effects of other, more drastic mutations. Modifying genes have been of the utmost importance in evolution, where they play the same role that the final adjustments—planing, polishing, and so on—play in the construction of a machine. Two examples may illustrate this.

In the mouse the most common type of spotting is due to a recessive gene. All homozygotes for this gene are spotted; but the degree of spotting is determined by modifying genes and may vary from almost self-colored to almost white. A mouse fancier can increase or decrease the amount of white spotting in his strain by always breeding from the most or least spotted animals, that is, from animals carrying the largest number of modifying genes of the right kind. In nature, natural selection often produces the finer adaptations of a species to its environment by the accumulation of modifying genes.

When a new mutant character makes its first appearance, it usually reduces drastically the viability of its carriers. It is a common experience of geneticists that such mutant strains may regain full viability in the course of several generations during which always the strongest individuals are selected for breeding. This breeding procedure results in an accumulation of modifying genes which "buffer" the adverse effects of the drastic mutation. Buffering genes must have played a major role in evolution.

3. The misconception that mutations affect only superficial characters which cannot be of great importance in evolution derives likewise from the fact that the early geneticists studied the laws of inheritance on easily observable characters like flower color in peas or wing shape in Drosophila. To a reader of the preceding chapters it must be obvious that all characters, even the most essential ones, are subject to mutation. Essential enzymes may be lost by mutation (Chap. 23). Alternatively, strains of microorganisms that have lost such enzymes may regain them by "reverse mutation." Mutations that change the flowering habits of plants (Chap. 16, Fig. 44) form the basis for adaptations to the short summer days of the tropics or the long ones of the temperate zones. Mutations to webbed toes occur occasionally in man; they must have played an important role in the evolution of water-living animals (see p. 255). It is evident that mutations affecting vital structures or functions must often be lethal (Chap. 8), and cannot therefore be detected without special embryological investigations. Mutations that suppress the formation of the spine occur in mice, but embryos that are homozygous for the mutant gene die at a very early stage.

There is thus no reason to doubt that naturally occurring mutation, followed in most cases by genetic recombination, has been an adequate and sufficient source of the genetic variability required for evolution. Before the rediscovery of Mendel's laws this was, however, not realized, mainly because hereditary differences were attributed to differences of "the blood" and crossing was considered to result in "blood mixture." These terms still persist, although they have lost their meaning. This concept of heredity led to serious difficulties for a Darwinistic interpretation of evolution. When two fluids, say red and black ink, are mixed, their distinguishing properties are lost in the mixture and cannot be recovered by un-mixing. If hereditary differences reside in the blood, then they will be diluted and eventually lost by crossing, and a sufficient supply of genetic variability can be maintained only if new hereditary differences arise constantly at an unbelievably high frequency. Mendel's experiments removed with one stroke this obstacle to Darwinism by showing that hereditary differences are based on genes, which persist in crosses and may segregate out un-altered after untold generations. Unfortunately, Darwin, although a contemporary of Mendel, did not know of these experiments. He therefore felt it necessary to water down his concept of evolution by admitting that the chance origin of hereditary differences was not the only source of genetical variability. In the search for an additional source he went back to older ideas, in particular to the theory of Lamarck, a famous French biologist. Lamarck had been impressed by the ability of organisms to adapt to the requirements of their environment and mode of life. A blacksmith develops strong arm muscles through exercise; young trees in dense planta-tions grow high in the search for light; fur-bearing animals have a thicker fur in winter than in summer. Lamarck assumed that such individually acquired adaptive characters are inherited so that, for instance, animals that have strengthened their leg muscles through running would give birth to young in whom the leg muscles from the very start are better developed than in newborn young from less active parents. This theory has now been abandoned by the vast majority of geneticists west of the Iron Curtain. Attempts to pro-vide experimental evidence for the "inheritance of acquired charac-ters" have never been successful. It would, indeed, be difficult to explain how the acquisition of, in the above instance, well-developed leg muscles could act on the germ cells in such a way as to produce mutations that ensure good development of the same muscles in the offspring. Evidently it is not possible to predict with absolute certainty that a given type of experiment will never give a positive result. If the few remaining adherents of Lamarckism should ever produce proof for the inheritance of an acquired character, this discovery would have to be fitted into our concepts of genetics and evolution. This, however, would hardly effect great changes in our present interpretation of evolution. The application of mathematical methods to the study of evolution has shown that the existing forces of mutation, recombination, and natural selection can account adequately for the speed and pattern of evolution, so that any additional causes of genetic variability can at best have played only a minor role in providing material for the grandi-

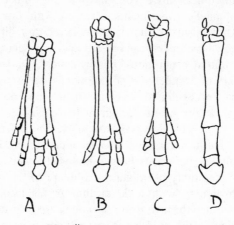

A = over 50 million years ago
B = over 30 million years ago
C = less than 20 million years ago
D = from I million years ago to the present time

FIG. 84.
Evolution of the forefoot in the horse.

ose progression of forms of life from the simplest "living molecules" to the present abundance and variety of living forms.

Still a different force of evolution is often evoked by paleontologists, that is, by scientists who study the record of the fossils. Many of these scientists believe that, once a group of organisms has started along a new evolutionary path, a special directive force will see to it that this path is pursued undeviatingly through long periods of evolution. It is easy to understand how this belief arose. Figure 84 shows the evolution of the forefoot of the horse over the past fifty million years. All this time there has been a faithfully continued trend toward making the feet of these animals better and better adapted to fleet running across the prairie. In other cases, the same inexorable force seems to have guided groups of organisms along their chosen paths unto the bitter end of extinction. Prehistoric animals in certain lines became larger and larger or developed more and more bizarre horns right up to the moment when the line broke off abruptly. For a nongeneticist it is difficult to understand how such clear trends can arise from selection acting on chance mutations and recombinations. We must, however, consider that, although mutation and recombination are chance events, selection is not. It is oriented by two sets of conditions: the environment to which the organism has to adapt and the structure of the organism itself. Different organisms adapt to their environment in quite different ways. On the same patch of beach you may see wading birds that strut about on long thin legs with widespread toes and ducks that waddle ashore on short bent legs with webbed feet. This type of specialization into waders and swimmers can be traced back far into the evolutionary history of birds. Once a group of birds with moderately long legs had started to search for food on beaches, any mutation that made the bones of legs and feet longer and thinner would be of advantage and would spread through the group as a result of natural selection. On the contrary, mutations that made the leg bones shorter or produced webbing of the toes would be disadvantageous and would soon disappear again. The closer an organism is to perfect adaptation the smaller the number of changes that still are advantageous, and the narrower and straighter becomes the path of its evolution. A traveler may approach a distant town by a variety of roads; once he has chosen his main road, his choice of side roads has become restricted; at the last crossroads his choice is no longer free. These considerations—together with others that cannot be discussed here —make it unnecessary to evoke a mystical directive force for the explanation of evolutionary trends.

Naturalists, including Darwin himself, have pointed out a further difficulty to the interpretation of evolution by natural selection. This is the persistence in many species of characters without apparent adaptive value, of—so to speak—frills of evolution like the different patterns on butterflies' wings or the different blood groups in man. Each such case poses its own question. Among the anwers, two only may be mentioned. Firstly, characters may possess selective advantages that are not obvious to the casual observer. English students of evolution have found that the variety of banding patterns in certain land snails permits nice adaptation to a variety of backgrounds—woods, hedgerows, meadows—and serves as camouflage against attacks by thrushes. Secondly, the majority of genes have pleiotropic effects (Chap. 23). A useless or even a harmful character may be controlled by a gene with less obvious pleiotropic effects of selective value. A striking example is the preservation of the gene for sickle cell anemia (Chap. 23) in the human species. Investigations that have been started recently suggest that the human blood groups, too, may have pleiotropic effects controlling susceptibility or resistance to certain diseases. It may be pertinent to add that there is absolutely no ground for suspecting that the genes for human skin color have pleiotropic effects on any character of social significance.

There remains one major problem to which Darwin himself drew attention. In his *Origin of Species* he asks: "Why, if species have descended from other species by fine gradations, do we not everywhere see transitional forms?" In answer he gave a number of possible reasons for the lack of transitional forms, the most important being that "the very process of natural selection constantly tends . . . to exterminate . . . the intermediate links." For Darwin, who did not know the laws of gene segregation and recombination, this was a plausible explanation; for us it is not. We regard intermediate forms as the result of chance gene combinations which are as easily broken up again as they were formed. The further evolution of intermediate into even better adapted forms would not have been possible without mechanisms for holding together the initially formed favorable gene combinations. Such mechanisms are called "isolating mechanisms." Like sex and diploidy, they are results as well as causes of evolution. They may be of many different kinds, but all achieve the same purpose: the restriction or prevention of crossing and genetic recombination between the original group and any subgroup within which an advantageous genotype has spread to a sufficient number of individuals. Only a few examples of isolating mechanisms can be mentioned here. In plants, mutations changing the time of flowering will prevent cross-fertilization between the mutant form and the strain from which it arose. In plant-eating insects, the same is achieved by mutations that alter the choice of host plant. In animals, mutations affecting the sex organs or mating behavior may prevent successful pairing. Where crosses are possible, the progeny may be sterile: horse and donkey produce live progeny with each other, but mules and hinnies are sterile. The most common isolating mechanism is geographical isolation. When sufficient individuals within a population have acquired a new combination of genes they may become able to colonize new territory in which the original forms cannot survive. This must have happened repeatedly in the early periods of evolution when life first emerged from the ocean onto land, and again later, when land-living organisms like mammals split off groups like seals or whales that resettled to life in the ocean. In such cases genetical differences preceded geographical isolation. More often the sequence will have been the opposite: a new geographical barrier such as a mountain, a gorge, or an arm of the sea divided a population of organisms into two groups between which mating and the exchange of genes was no longer possible. In each of these groups natural selection then favored those particular mutations and gene combinations that were most suitable to the particular environment. Since no two environments are quite alike, this led inevitably to an increasing genetical divergence between the groups, and this in turn often resulted in differences of organization or behavior that maintained the isolation even when the barrier subsequently was removed. At this stage isolation had become complete. Two groups are called separate species when they are no longer able to interbreed and produce fertile progeny with one another.

With the formation of partially or wholly isolated groups natural selection entered a new stage. Instead of acting only on individuals, it now came to act on groups, allowing some of them to spread while others dwindled and finally disappeared. Wherever groups of organisms compete for food, for air, for space, for light, or for anything else that is essential to survival and reproduction, selection between groups takes first rank over selection between individuals within groups. This has had important consequences. No longer can the value of the individual be measured solely by its ability to reproduce offspring and transmit its genes to posterity; more important than this is the individual's contribution to survival and competing ability of the group. Worker bees are sterile; yet life and survival of the hive depends on their activities, and where colonies of wild bees compete for food it is the sterile workers and not the fertile drones that decide the issue. In colonies of termites and ants, highly specialized castes of sterile workers and soldiers have evolved through natural selection acting on groups rather than individuals. During periods of expansion in human history, success in competition for land depended to a large extent on the fertility of individuals. Once a society has settled, its further development, competing ability, and survival are no longer determined by its most prolific, but by its most intelligent, resourceful, energetic, and socially minded individuals. In the Middle Ages the care of the sick, the pursuit of knowledge, and the education of the young was mainly in the hands of childless nuns and monks. In our own time it has become a slogan to say that the state with the most highly developed science and technology will rule the earth; yet scientists and teachers are not usually the most prolific members of society. Similarly, aggressiveness is an asset in the competition between individuals, but survival of a group may be endangered by aggressiveness of its members. Conversely, helpfulness, sympathy, unselfishness are harmful to the individual in its struggle for survival but beneficial to the group as a whole; selection between groups will favor those in which these attitudes are prevalent.

For selection acting on groups, the over-all gene content of the group as a whole is its decisive feature. If a group contains many genes for a high IQ (Chap. 18), then it will have many intelligent members and its average intelligence will be high; if it contains few such genes, its average intelligence will be low. The total gene content of a group is often called its "gene pool." If we return to our simile of genes as playing cards (Chap. 19), we may imagine the gene pool as containing all the hands owned by all the individuals that constitute the group. The number of cards will, of course, depend only on the number of individuals in the group, for—according to the rules of the game—every individual has two cards of every kind. But the way the cards can be assigned to sets need not be the same in each pool and will, indeed, not be the same when the groups are partially or wholly isolated. Thus in one pool the aces may be distributed evenly over the four sets;

in another the ace of clubs may be ten times as frequent as the ace of hearts and twice as frequent as the two other aces taken together; in still another the ace of spades may be missing altogether. The individuals born into the group "draw" their cards from the pool, and this limits and controls the possible hands they may acquire. If the ace of spades is not in the pool, it cannot be drawn by any individual; if the ace of clubs is ten times as frequent as the ace of hearts, its chance of being drawn is ten times as high.

In this picture the degree of isolation between two groups is represented by the frequency with which the pools exchange cards, that is, the frequency with which cards from one pool are carried into the other either because an individual changes groups or because the two parents of an individual come from different groups. The oftener the pools exchange cards the more will their differences even out. When exchange is frequent, both pools will contain similar card mixtures. When exchange has become so frequent that any individual is as likely to draw its cards from either pool, the two pools have merged into one common pool in which the cards of both have been combined into an evenly distributed mixture. In genetical language we may express this by saying that the frequency of gene exchange through immigration and crossbreeding determines the degree of isolation and, through this, the degree of divergence between two groups. Species are wholly isolated from one another. There is no gene exchange between them, and their genetic differences are manifold and profound.

Mankind is one large species, subdivided into groups all of which can exchange genes by crossbreeding but may be prevented from doing so by more or less effective barriers to marriage outside the group, such as geographical distance, caste and class systems, or religious differences. When minor groups are merged by, for instance, improved means of transport or a more liberal attitude toward differences of class or religion, harmful recessives are driven underground and the result is eugenically advantageous (Chap. 13). The largest and phenotypically more distinct human groups are called "races." Isolation between races was originally geographical and is still largely so. Where the geographical barrier has disappeared, a more or less rigorous isolation is often maintained by racial prejudice. The ancient and strict isolation between races has resulted in marked divergence between their gene pools. Some genes, for instance those for black or brown skin color, are represented by one particular allele in certain gene pools and by a different allele in others. The gene pool of Negroes contains only alleles for black skin color, the gene pool of Europeans contains only the alternative alleles for light color. By the effects of such genes every individual of one race can be distinguished from every individual of another. The number of such genes is, however, small. The majority of genes are represented by the same alleles in most or all races and differ only in the proportions in which these alleles are mixed in the gene pools. With the exception of some American Indian tribes, all human races carry the three blood group alleles, *A, B* and *O* (Chap. 10); but while *O* is the most common allele in all races, *B* is more frequent among Asiatics than among Europeans. Again, tasters and nontasters (Chap. 9) have been found in all tested races; but 94 per cent of North American Indians and only 70 per cent of North American Whites are tasters. In regard to these genes the races overlap, and members of different races may be alike while members of the same race may differ. There can be little doubt that races differ also in the frequencies of genes controlling mental abilities and personality traits. In which way and to what degree they do so cannot be decided from the scanty and inconclusive evidence available (Chap. 18). There is, however, no reason to believe that any one race has the privilege of carrying all the superior alleles of such genes, while other races carry mainly the inferior ones. On the contrary, there is every reason to believe that this is not so and that all races have their share of superior and inferior alleles.

In the long run, improved means of transport and spread of education are bound to remove the genetical barriers between races, although this process may be much delayed by geographical and social obstacles. Its over-all genetical outcome is difficult to predict. At present, all too many children from mixed marriages are handicapped by unfavorable environmental conditions. Where this is not so, beautiful and gifted chidren have often resulted from race crosses. Until children from mixed marriages can grow up in circumstances similar to those of children born to parents of like race no general assessment of the value of race crosses is possible.

Only one thing is certain. The exchange of genes between pools that have been separated for such a long time will engender a wealth of new variability. If, by that time, man has learned to take a hand in directing his own evolution he may find both challenge and opportunity in this diversity.

Reading List

This short list is intended as a help for those readers who want to go on to more advanced textbooks (1 and 2) or wish more information on special subjects. It had to be chosen from a fairly large number of books on genetics and evolution and is necessarily very incomplete.

1. Sinnott, E.W., L.C. Dunn and Th. Dobzhansky. *Principles of Genetics,* 5th ed. McGraw-Hill Co., New York, 1958.
2. Srb, A.M., and R.D. Owen. *General Genetics.* Freeman and Co., San Francisco, 1952.
3. Roberts, Fraser. *Medical Genetics.* Oxford University Press, 1959.
4. Penrose, L.S. *Outline of Human Genetics.* Heinemann, London, 1959.
5. Dunn, L.C. *Heredity and Evolution in Human Populations.* Harvard University Press, Cambridge, 1959.
6. Simpson, G.G. *The Meaning of Evolution.* Oxford University Press, 1950.
7. Haskell, G. *Practical Heredity with Drosophila.* Oliver and Boyd, London, 1960.
8. *The Biological Effects of Atomic Radiation.* Summary Reports from a Study by the National Academy of Sciences. National Research Council, Washington, D.C., 1956, 1960.

Index

harper ✦ torchbooks

HUMANITIES AND SOCIAL SCIENCES

American Studies

JOHN R. ALDEN: The American Revolution, 1775-1783. *Illus.*　TB/3011

RAY A. BILLINGTON: The Far Western Frontier, 1830-1860. *Illus.*　TB/3012

RANDOLPH S. BOURNE: The War and the Intellectuals: *A Collection of Essays, 1915-1919. Edited with an Introduction by Carl Resek*　TB/3043

JOSEPH CHARLES: The Origins of the American Party System　TB/1049

T. C. COCHRAN & WILLIAM MILLER: The Age of Enterprise: *A Social History of Industrial America*　TB/1054

FOSTER RHEA DULLES: America's Rise to World Power, 1898-1954. *Illus.*　TB/3021

W. A. DUNNING: Reconstruction, Political and Economic, 1865-1877　TB/1073

CLEMENT EATON: The Growth of Southern Civilization, 1790-1860. *Illus.*　TB/3040

HAROLD U. FAULKNER: Politics, Reform and Expansion, 1890-1900. *Illus.*　TB/3020

LOUIS FILLER: The Crusade against Slavery, 1830-1860. *Illus.*　TB/3029

EDITORS OF FORTUNE: America in the Sixties: *the Economy and the Society. Two-color charts*　TB/1015

LAWRENCE HENRY GIPSON: The Coming of the Revolution, 1763-1775. *Illus.*　TB/3007

FRANCIS J. GRUND: Aristocracy in America: *Jacksonian Democracy*　TB/1001

OSCAR HANDLIN, Editor: This Was America: *As Recorded by European Travelers to the Western Shore in the Eighteenth, Nineteenth, and Twentieth Centuries. Illus.*　TB/1119

MARCUS LEE HANSEN: The Atlantic Migration: 1607-1860. *Edited by Arthur M. Schlesinger; Introduction by Oscar Handlin*　TB/1052

MARCUS LEE HANSEN: The Immigrant in American History. *Edited with a Foreword by Arthur Schlesinger, Sr.*　TB/1120

JOHN D. HICKS: Republican Ascendancy, 1921-1933.* *Iilus.*　TB/3041

JOHN HIGHAM, Ed.: The Reconstruction of American History　TB/1068

ROBERT H. JACKSON: The Supreme Court in the American System of Government　TB/1106

JOHN F. KENNEDY: A Nation of Immigrants. *Illus.*　TB/1118

WILLIAM E. LEUCHTENBURG: Franklin D. Roosevelt and the New Deal, 1932-1940. *Illus.*　TB/3025

LEONARD W. LEVY: Freedom of Speech and Press in Early American History: *Legacy of Suppression*　TB/1109

ARTHUR S. LINK: Woodrow Wilson and the Progressive Era, 1910-1917. *Illus.*　TB/3023

BERNARD MAYO: Myths and Men: *Patrick Henry, George Washington, Thomas Jefferson*　TB/1108

JOHN C. MILLER: The Federalist Era, 1789-1801.* *Illus.*　TB/3027

PERRY MILLER & T. H. JOHNSON, Editors: The Puritans: *A Sourcebook of Their Writings*
　　　　Volume I　TB/1093
　　　　Volume II　TB/1094

GEORGE E. MOWRY: The Era of Theodore Roosevelt and the Birth of Modern America, 1900-1912.* *Illus.*　TB/3022

WALLACE NOTESTEIN: The English People on the Eve of Colonization, 1603-1630. *Illus.*　TB/3006

RUSSEL BLAINE NYE: The Cultural Life of the New Nation, 1776-1801. *Illus.*　TB/3026

GEORGE E. PROBST, Ed.: The Happy Republic: *A Reader in Tocqueville's America*　TB/1060

FRANK THISTLETHWAITE: America and the Atlantic Community: *Anglo-American Aspects, 1790-1850*　TB/1107

TWELVE SOUTHERNERS: I'll Take My Stand: *The South and the Agrarian Tradition. Introduction by Louis D. Rubin, Jr.; Biographical Essays by Virginia Rock*　TB/1072

A. F. TYLER: Freedom's Ferment: *Phases of American Social History from the Revolution to the Outbreak of the Civil War. Illus.*　TB/1074

GLYNDON G. VAN DEUSEN: The Jacksonian Era, 1828-1848. *Illus.*　TB/3028

WALTER E. WEYL: The New Democracy: *An Essay on Certain Political and Economic Tendencies in the United States*　TB/3042

LOUIS B. WRIGHT: The Cultural Life of the American Colonies, 1607-1763. *Illus.*　TB/3005

LOUIS B. WRIGHT: Culture on the Moving Frontier　TB/1053

Anthropology & Sociology

W. E. LE GROS CLARK: The Antecedents of Man: *An Introduction to the Evolution of the Primates. Illus.*　TB/559

ST. CLAIR DRAKE & HORACE R. CAYTON: Black Metropolis: *A Study of Negro Life in a Northern City. Introduction by Everett C. Hughes. Tables, maps, charts and graphs*
　　　　Volume I　TB/1086
　　　　Volume II　TB/1087

CORA DU BOIS: The People of Alor. *New Preface by the author. Illus.*
　　　　Volume I　TB/1042
　　　　Volume II　TB/1043

L. S. B. LEAKEY: Adam's Ancestors: *The Evolution of Man and his Culture. Illus.*　TB/1019

ROBERT H. LOWIE: Primitive Society. *Introduction by Fred Eggan*　TB/1056

TALCOTT PARSONS & EDWARD A. SHILS, Editors: Toward a General Theory of Action: *Theoretical Foundations for the Social Sciences*　TB/1083

SIR EDWARD TYLOR: The Origins of Culture. *Part I of "Primitive Culture." Introduction by Paul Radin*　TB/33

SIR EDWARD TYLOR: Religion in Primitive Culture. *Part II of "Primitive Culture." Introduction by Paul Radin*　TB/34

W. LLOYD WARNER: Social Class in America: *The Evaluation of Status*　TB/1013

*The New American Nation Series, edited by Henry Steele Commager and Richard B. Morris.

Art and Art History

EMILE MÂLE: The Gothic Image: *Religious Art in France of the Thirteenth Century. 190 illus.*   TB/44

ERWIN PANOFSKY: Studies in Iconology: *Humanistic Themes in the Art of the Renaissance. 180 illustrations*   TB/1077

ALEXANDRE PIANKOFF: The Shrines of Tut-Ankh-Amon. *Edited by N. Rambova. 117 illus.*   TB/2011

JEAN SEZNEC: The Survival of the Pagan Gods: *The Mythological Tradition and Its Place in Renaissance Humanism and Art. 108 illustrations*   TB/2004

HEINRICH ZIMMER: Myths and Symbols in Indian Art and Civilization: *70 illustrations*   TB/2005

Business, Economics & Economic History

REINHARD BENDIX: Work and Authority in Industry: *Ideologies of Management in the Course of Industrialization*   TB/3035

THOMAS C. COCHRAN: The American Business System: *A Historical Perspective, 1900-1955*   TB/1080

ROBERT DAHL & CHARLES E. LINDBLOM: Politics, Economics, and Welfare: *Planning and Politico-Economic Systems Resolved into Basic Social Processes*   TB/3037

PETER F. DRUCKER: The New Society: *The Anatomy of Industrial Order*   TB/1082

ROBERT L. HEILBRONER: The Great Ascent: *The Struggle for Economic Development*   TB/3030

PAUL MANTOUX: The Industrial Revolution in the Eighteenth Century: *The Beginnings of the Modern Factory System in England*   TB/1079

WILLIAM MILLER, Ed.: Men in Business: *Essays on the Historical Role of the Entrepreneur*   TB/1081

PERRIN STRYKER: The Character of the Executive: *Eleven Studies in Managerial Qualities*   TB/1041

PIERRE URI: Partnership for Progress.   TB/3036

Contemporary Culture

JACQUES BARZUN: The House of Intellect   TB/1051

JOHN U. NEF: Cultural Foundations of Industrial Civilization   TB/1024

PAUL VALÉRY: The Outlook for Intelligence   TB/2016

History: General

L. CARRINGTON GOODRICH: A Short History of the Chinese People. *Illus.*   TB/3015

DAN N. JACOBS & HANS BAERWALD: Chinese Communism: *Selected Documents*   TB/3031

BERNARD LEWIS: The Arabs in History   TB/1029

SIR PERCY SYKES: A History of Exploration. *Introduction by John K. Wright*   TB/1046

History: Ancient and Medieval

A. ANDREWES: The Greek Tyrants   TB/1103

HELEN CAM: England before Elizabeth   TB/1026

NORMAN COHN: The Pursuit of the Millennium: *Revolutionary Messianism in medieval and Reformation Europe and its bearing on modern totalitarian movements*   TB/1037

G. G. COULTON: Medieval Village, Manor, and Monastery   TB/1022

F. L. GANSHOF: Feudalism   TB/1058

J. M. HUSSEY: The Byzantine World   TB/1057

SAMUEL NOAH KRAMER: Sumerian Mythology   TB/1055

FERDINAND LOT: The End of the Ancient World and the Beginnings of the Middle Ages. *Introduction by Glanville Downey*   TB/1044

J. M. WALLACE-HADRILL: The Barbarian West: *The Early Middle Ages, A.D. 400-1000*   TB/1061

History: Renaissance & Reformation

JACOB BURCKHARDT: The Civilization of the Renaissance in Italy. *Introduction by Benjamin Nelson and Charles Trinkaus. Illus.*   Volume I   TB/40
    Volume II   TB/41

ERNST CASSIRER: The Individual and the Cosmos in Renaissance Philosophy. *Translated with an Introduction by Mario Domandi*   TB/1097

EDWARD P. CHEYNEY: The Dawn of a New Era, 1250-1453 †*Illus.*   TB/3002

WALLACE K. FERGUSON, et al.: Facets of the Renaissance   TB/1098

WALLACE K. FERGUSON, et al.: The Renaissance: *Six Essays. Illus.*   TB/1084

MYRON P. GILMORE: The World of Humanism, 1453-1517. †*Illus.*   TB/3003

JOHAN HUIZINGA: Erasmus and the Age of Reformation. *Illus.*   TB/19

PAUL O. KRISTELLER: Renaissance Thought: *The Classic, Scholastic, and Humanist Strains*   TB/1048

NICCOLÒ MACHIAVELLI: History of Florence and of the Affairs of Italy: *from the earliest times to the death of Lorenzo the Magnificent. Introduction by Felix Gilbert*   TB/1027

ALFRED VON MARTIN: Sociology of the Renaissance. *Introduction by W. K. Ferguson*   TB/1099

J. E. NEALE: The Age of Catherine de Medici   TB/1085

ERWIN PANOFSKY: Studies in Iconology: *Humanistic Themes in the Art of the Renaissance. 180 illustrations*   TB/1077

J. H. PARRY: The Establishment of the European Hegemony: 1415-1715: *Trade and Exploration in the Age of the Renaissance*   TB/1045

HENRI PIRENNE: Early Democracies in the Low Countries: *Urban Society and Political Conflict in the Middle Ages and the Renaissance. Introduction by John H. Mundy*   TB/1110

FERDINAND SCHEVILL: The Medici. *Illus.*   TB/1010

FERDINAND SCHEVILL: Medieval and Renaissance Florence. *Illus.* Volume I: *Medieval Florence* TB/1090
Volume II: *The Coming of Humanism and the Age of the Medici*   TB/1091

G. M. TREVELYAN: England in the Age of Wycliffe, 1368-1520   TB/1112

VESPASIANO: Renaissance Princes, Popes, and Prelates: *The Vespasiano Memoirs: Lives of Illustrious Men of the XVth Century. Introduction by Myron P. Gilmore. Illus.*   TB/1111

History: Modern European

FREDERICK B. ARTZ: Reaction and Revolution, 1815-1832. †*Illus.*   TB/3034

MAX BELOFF: The Age of Absolutism, 1660-1815   TB/1062

ROBERT C. BINKLEY: Realism and Nationalism, 1852-1871. †*Illus.*   TB/3038

CRANE BRINTON: A Decade of Revolution, 1789-1799. †*Illus.*   TB/3018

†*The Rise of Modern Europe Series,* edited by William L. Langer.

J. BRONOWSKI & BRUCE MAZLISH: The Western Intellectual Tradition: *From Leonardo to Hegel* TB/3001

GEOFFREY BRUUN: Europe and the French Imperium, 1799-1814. †*Illus.* TB/3033

WALTER L. DORN: Competition for Empire, 1740-1763. †*Illus.* TB/3032

CARL J. FRIEDRICH: The Age of the Baroque, 1610-1660. †*Illus.* TB/3004

LEO GERSHOY: From Despotism to Revolution, 1763-1789. †*Illus.* TB/3017

ALBERT GOODWIN: The French Revolution TB/1064

CARLTON J. H. HAYES: A Generation of Materialism, 1871-1900. †*Illus.* TB/3039

J. H. HEXTER: Reappraisals in History: *New Views on History and Society in Early Modern Europe* TB/1100

A. R. HUMPHREYS: The Augustan World: *Society, Thought, and Letters in Eighteenth Century England* TB/1105

DAN N. JACOBS, Ed.: The New Communist Manifesto and Related Documents TB/1078

HANS KOHN, Ed.: The Mind of Modern Russia: *Historical and Political Thought of Russia's Great Age* TB/1065

SIR LEWIS NAMIER: Vanished Supremacies: *Essays on European History, 1812-1918* TB/1088

JOHN U. NEF: Western Civilization Since the Renaissance: *Peace, War, Industry, and the Arts* TB/1113

FREDERICK L. NUSSBAUM: The Triumph of Science and Reason, 1660-1685. †*Illus.* TB/3009

RAYMOND W. POSTGATE, Ed.: Revolution from 1789 to 1906: *Selected Documents* TB/1063

PENFIELD ROBERTS: The Quest for Security, 1715-1740. †*Illus.* TB/3016

PRISCILLA ROBERTSON: Revolutions of 1848: *A Social History* TB/1025

N. N. SUKHANOV: The Russian Revolution, 1917: *Eyewitness Account.* Edited by Joel Carmichael
Volume I TB/1066
Volume II TB/1067

JOHN B. WOLF: The Emergence of the Great Powers, 1685-1715. †*Illus.* TB/3010

JOHN B. WOLF: France: 1814-1919: *The Rise of a Liberal-Democratic Society* TB/3019

Intellectual History

HERSCHEL BAKER: The Image of Man: *A Study of the Idea of Human Dignity in Classical Antiquity, the Middle Ages, and the Renaissance* TB/1047

J. BRONOWSKI & BRUCE MAZLISH: The Western Intellectual Tradition: *From Leonardo to Hegel* TB/3001

NORMAN COHN: The Pursuit of the Millennium: *Revolutionary Messianism in medieval and Reformation Europe and its bearing on modern totalitarian movements* TB/1037

ARTHUR O. LOVEJOY: The Great Chain of Being: *A Study of the History of an Idea* TB/1009

ROBERT PAYNE: Hubris: *A Study of Pride.* Foreword by Sir Herbert Read TB/1031

BRUNO SNELL: The Discovery of the Mind: *The Greek Origins of European Thought* TB/1018

Literature, Poetry, The Novel & Criticism

JAMES BAIRD: Ishmael: *The Art of Melville in the Contexts of International Primitivism* TB/1023

JACQUES BARZUN: The House of Intellect TB/1051

W. J. BATE: From Classic to Romantic: *Premises of Taste in Eighteenth Century England* TB/1036

RACHEL BESPALOFF: On the Iliad TB/2006

R. P. BLACKMUR, et al.: Lectures in Criticism. *Introduction by Huntington Cairns* TB/2003

ABRAHAM CAHAN: The Rise of David Levinsky: *a novel.* Introduction by John Higham TB/1028

ERNST R. CURTIUS: European Literature and the Latin Middle Ages TB/2015

GEORGE ELIOT: Daniel Deronda: *a novel.* Introduction by F. R. Leavis TB/1039

ETIENNE GILSON: Dante and Philosophy TB/1089

ALFRED HARBAGE: As They Liked It: *A Study of Shakespeare's Moral Artistry* TB/1035

STANLEY R. HOPPER, Ed.: Spiritual Problems in Contemporary Literature TB/21

A. R. HUMPHREYS: The Augustan World: *Society, Thought, and Letters in Eighteenth Century England* TB/1105

ALDOUS HUXLEY: Antic Hay & The Gioconda Smile. TB/3503

ALDOUS HUXLEY: Brave New World & Brave New World Revisited. *Introduction by C. P. Snow* TB/3501

ALDOUS HUXLEY: Point Counter Point. *Introduction by C. P. Snow* TB/3502

HENRY JAMES: The Princess Casamassima: *a novel.* Introduction by Clinton F. Oliver TB/1005

HENRY JAMES: Roderick Hudson: *a novel.* Introduction by Leon Edel TB/1016

HENRY JAMES: The Tragic Muse: *a novel.* Introduction by Leon Edel TB/1017

ARNOLD KETTLE: An Introduction to the English Novel. Volume I: *Defoe to George Eliot* TB/1011
Volume II: *Henry James to the Present* TB/1012

JOHN STUART MILL: On Bentham and Coleridge. *Introduction by F. R. Leavis* TB/1070

PERRY MILLER & T. H. JOHNSON, Editors: The Puritans: *A Sourcebook of Their Writings*
Volume I TB/1093
Volume II TB/1094

KENNETH B. MURDOCK: Literature and Theology in Colonial New England TB/99

SAMUEL PEPYS: The Diary of Samuel Pepys. Edited by O. F. Morshead. Illustrations by Ernest Shepard TB/1007

ST.-JOHN PERSE: Seamarks TB/2002

O. E. RÖLVAAG: Giants in the Earth. *Introduction by Einar Haugen* TB/3504

GEORGE SANTAYANA: Interpretations of Poetry and Religion TB/9

C. P. SNOW: Time of Hope: *a novel* TB/1040

DOROTHY VAN GHENT: The English Novel: *Form and Function* TB/1050

E. B. WHITE: One Man's Meat. *Introduction by Walter Blair* TB/3505

MORTON DAUWEN ZABEL, Editor: Literary Opinion in America
Volume I TB/3013
Volume II TB/3014

Myth, Symbol & Folklore

JOSEPH CAMPBELL, Editor: Pagan and Christian Mysteries TB/2013

MIRCEA ELIADE: Cosmos and History: *The Myth of the Eternal Return* TB/2050

C. G. JUNG & C. KERÉNYI: Essays on a Science of Mythology: *The Myths of the Divine Child and the Divine Maiden* TB/2014

ERWIN PANOFSKY: Studies in Iconology: *Humanistic Themes in the Art of the Renaissance. 180 illustrations* TB/1077

JEAN SEZNEC: The Survival of the Pagan Gods: *The Mythological Tradition and its Place in Renaissance Humanism and Art. 108 illustrations* TB/2004

HEINRICH ZIMMER: Myths and Symbols in Indian Art and Civilization. *70 illustrations* TB/2005

Philosophy

HENRI BERGSON: Time and Free Will: *An Essay on the Immediate Data of Consciousness* TB/1021

H. J. BLACKHAM: Six Existentialist Thinkers: *Kierkegaard, Nietzsche, Jaspers, Marcel, Heidegger, Sartre* TB/1002

ERNST CASSIRER: Rousseau, Kant and Goethe. *Introduction by Peter Gay* TB/1092

FREDERICK COPLESTON: Medieval Philosophy TB/76

F. M. CORNFORD: From Religion to Philosophy: *A Study in the Origins of Western Speculation* TB/20

WILFRID DESAN: The Tragic Finale: *An Essay on the Philosophy of Jean-Paul Sartre* TB/1030

PAUL FRIEDLANDER: Plato: *An Introduction* TB/2017

ETIENNE GILSON: Dante and Philosophy TB/1089

WILLIAM CHASE GREENE: Moira: *Fate, Good, and Evil in Greek Thought* TB/1104

W. K. C. GUTHRIE: The Greek Philosophers: *From Thales to Aristotle* TB/1008

F. H. HEINEMANN: Existentialism and the Modern Predicament TB/28

IMMANUEL KANT: The Doctrine of Virtue, *being Part II of The Metaphysic of Morals. Translated with Notes and Introduction by Mary J. Gregor. Foreword by H. J. Paton* TB/110

IMMANUEL KANT: Lectures on Ethics. *Introduction by Lewis W. Beck* TB/105

WILLARD VAN ORMAN QUINE: From a Logical Point of View: *Logico-Philosophical Essays* TB/566

BERTRAND RUSSELL et al.: The Philosophy of Bertrand Russell. *Edited by Paul Arthur Schilpp*
Volume I TB/1095
Volume II TB/1096

L. S. STEBBING: A Modern Introduction to Logic TB/538

ALFRED NORTH WHITEHEAD: Process and Reality: *An Essay in Cosmology* TB/1033

WILHELM WINDELBAND: A History of Philosophy I: *Greek, Roman, Medieval* TB/38

WILHELM WINDELBAND: A History of Philosophy II: *Renaissance, Enlightenment, Modern* TB/39

Philosophy of History

NICOLAS BERDYAEV: The Beginning and the End TB/14

NICOLAS BERDYAEV: The Destiny of Man TB/61

WILHELM DILTHEY: Pattern and Meaning in History: *Thoughts on History and Society. Edited with an Introduction by H. P. Rickman* TB/1075

JOSE ORTEGA Y GASSET: The Modern Theme. *Introduction by Jose Ferrater Mora* TB/1038

H. J. PATON & RAYMOND KLIBANSKY, Eds.: Philosophy and History TB/1115

W. H. WALSH: Philosophy of History: *An Introduction* TB/1020

Political Science & Government

JEREMY BENTHAM: The Handbook of Political Fallacies: *Introduction by Crane Brinton* TB/1069

KENNETH E. BOULDING: Conflict and Defense: *A General Theory* TB/3024

CRANE BRINTON: English Political Thought in the Nineteenth Century TB/1071

ROBERT DAHL & CHARLES E. LINDBLOM: Politics, Economics, and Welfare: *Planning and Politico-Economic Systems Resolved into Basic Social Processes* TB/3037

JOHN NEVILLE FIGGIS: Political Thought from Gerson to Grotius: *1414-1625: Seven Studies. Introduction by Garrett Mattingly* TB/1032

F. L. GANSHOF: Feudalism TB/1058

G. P. GOOCH: English Democratic Ideas in the Seventeenth Century TB/1006

ROBERT H. JACKSON: The Supreme Court in the American System of Government TB/1106

KINGSLEY MARTIN: French Liberal Thought in the Eighteenth Century: *A Study of Political Ideas from Bayle to Condorcet* TB/1114

J. P. MAYER: Alexis de Tocqueville: *A Biographical Study in Political Science* TB/1014

JOHN STUART MILL: On Bentham and Coleridge. *Introduction by F. R. Leavis* TB/1070

JOHN B. MORRALL: Political Thought in Medieval Times TB/1076

KARL R. POPPER: The Open Society and Its Enemies
Volume I: *The Spell of Plato* TB/1101
Volume II: *The High Tide of Prophecy: Hegel, Marx, and the Aftermath* TB/1102

JOSEPH A. SCHUMPETER: Capitalism, Socialism and Democracy TB/3008

Psychology

ANTON T. BOISEN: The Exploration of the Inner World: *A Study of Mental Disorder and Religious Experience* TB/87

WALTER BROMBERG: The Mind of Man: *A History of Psychotherapy and Psychoanalysis* TB/1003

SIGMUND FREUD: On Creativity and the Unconscious: *Papers on the Psychology of Art, Literature, Love, Religion. Intro. by Benjamin Nelson* TB/45

C. JUDSON HERRICK: The Evolution of Human Nature TB/545

ALDOUS HUXLEY: The Devils of Loudun: *A Study in the Psychology of Power Politics and Mystical Religion in the France of Cardinal Richelieu* TB/60

WILLIAM JAMES: Psychology: *The Briefer Course. Edited with an Intro. by Gordon Allport* TB/1034

C. G. JUNG: Psychological Reflections. *Edited by Jolande Jacobi* TB/2001

C. G. JUNG: Symbols of Transformation: *An Analysis of the Prelude to a Case of Schizophrenia*
Volume I TB/2009
Volume II TB/2010

C. G. JUNG & C. KERÉNYI: Essays on a Science of Mythology: *The Myths of the Divine Child and the Divine Maiden* TB/2014

ERICH NEUMANN: Amor and Psyche: *The Psychic Development of the Feminine* TB/2012

ERICH NEUMANN: The Origins and History of Consciousness
Volume I *Illus.* TB/2007
Volume II TB/2008

RELIGION

Mathematics

H. DAVENPORT: The Higher Arithmetic: *An Introduction to the Theory of Numbers*   TB/526

H. G. FORDER: Geometry: *An Introduction*   TB/548

GOTTLOB FREGE: The Foundations of Arithmetic: *A Logico-Mathematical Enquiry into the Concept of Number*   TB/534

S. KÖRNER: The Philosophy of Mathematics: *An Introduction*   TB/547

D. E. LITTLEWOOD: Skeleton Key of Mathematics: *A Simple Account of Complex Algebraic Problems*   TB/525

GEORGE E. OWEN: Fundamentals of Scientific Mathematics   TB/569

WILLARD VAN ORMAN QUINE: Mathematical Logic   TB/558

O. G. SUTTON: Mathematics in Action. *Foreword by James R. Newman. Illus.*   TB/518

FREDERICK WAISMANN: Introduction to Mathematical Thinking. *Foreword by Karl Menger*   TB/511

Philosophy of Science

R. B. BRAITHWAITE: Scientific Explanation   TB/515

J. BRONOWSKI: Science and Human Values. *Illus.*   TB/505

ALBERT EINSTEIN: Philosopher-Scientist. *Edited by Paul A. Schilpp*   Volume I   TB/502
Volume II   TB/503

WERNER HEISENBERG: Physics and Philosophy: *The Revolution in Modern Science. Introduction by F. S. C. Northrop*   TB/549

JOHN MAYNARD KEYNES: A Treatise on Probability. *Introduction by N. R. Hanson*   TB/557

STEPHEN TOULMIN: Foresight and Understanding: *An Enquiry into the Aims of Science. Foreword by Jacques Barzun*   TB/564

STEPHEN TOULMIN: The Philosophy of Science: *An Introduction*   TB/513

W. H. WATSON: On Understanding Physics. *Introduction by Ernest Nagel*   TB/507

G. J. WHITROW: The Natural Philosophy of Time   TB/563

Physics and Cosmology

DAVID BOHM: Causality and Chance in Modern Physics. *Foreword by Louis de Broglie*   TB/536

P. W. BRIDGMAN: The Nature of Thermodynamics   TB/537

LOUIS DE BROGLIE: Physics and Microphysics. *Foreword by Albert Einstein*   TB/514

T. G. COWLING: Molecules in Motion: *An Introduction to the Kinetic Theory of Gases. Illus.*   TB/516

A. C. CROMBIE, Ed.: Turning Point in Physics   TB/535

C. V. DURELL: Readable Relativity. *Foreword by Freeman J. Dyson*   TB/530

ARTHUR EDDINGTON: Space, Time and Gravitation: *An outline of the General Relativity Theory*   TB/510

GEORGE GAMOW: Biography of Physics   TB/567

MAX JAMMER: Concepts of Force: *A Study in the Foundation of Dynamics*   TB/550

MAX JAMMER: Concepts of Space: *The History of Theories of Space in Physics. Foreword by Albert Einstein*   TB/533

EDMUND WHITTAKER: History of the Theories of Aether and Electricity
Volume I: *The Classical Theories*   TB/531
Volume II: *The Modern Theories*   TB/532

G. J. WHITROW: The Structure and Evolution of the Universe: *An Introduction to Cosmology. Illus.*   TB/504

A LETTER TO THE READER

Overseas, there is considerable belief that we are a country of extreme conservatism and that we cannot accommodate to social change.

Books about America in the hands of readers abroad can help change those ideas.

The U. S. Information Agency cannot, by itself, meet the vast need for books about the United States.

You can help.

Harper Torchbooks provides three packets of books on American history, economics, sociology, literature and politics to help meet the need.

To send a packet of Torchbooks [*] overseas, all you need do is send your check for $7 (which includes cost of shipping) to Harper & Row. The U. S. Information Agency will distribute the books to libraries, schools, and other centers all over the world.

I ask every American to support this program, part of a worldwide BOOKS USA campaign.

I ask you to share in the opportunity to help tell others about America.

EDWARD R. MURROW
Director,
U. S. Information Agency

[*retailing at $10.85 to $12.00]

PACKET I: *Twentieth Century America*

Dulles/America's Rise to World Power, 1898-1954
Cochran/The American Business System, 1900-1955
Zabel, Editor/Literary Opinion in America (two volumes)
Drucker/The New Society: *The Anatomy of Industrial Order*
Fortune Editors/America in the Sixties: *The Economy and the Society*

PACKET II: *American History*

Billington/The Far Western Frontier, 1830-1860
Mowry/The Era of Theodore Roosevelt and the
  Birth of Modern America, 1900-1912
Faulkner/Politics, Reform, and Expansion, 1890-1900
Cochran & Miller/The Age of Enterprise: *A Social History of
  Industrial America*
Tyler/Freedom's Ferment: *American Social History from the
  Revolution to the Civil War*

PACKET III: *American History*

Hansen/The Atlantic Migration, 1607-1860
Degler/Out of Our Past: *The Forces that Shaped Modern America*
Probst, Editor/The Happy Republic: *A Reader in Tocqueville's America*
Alden/The American Revolution, 1775-1783
Wright/The Cultural Life of the American Colonies, 1607-1763

*Your gift will be acknowledged directly to you by the overseas recipient.
Simply fill out the coupon, detach and mail with your check or money order.*

HARPER & ROW, PUBLISHERS · BOOKS USA DEPT.
49 East 33rd Street, New York 16, N. Y.

Packet I ☐   Packet II ☐   Packet III ☐

Please send the BOOKS USA library packet(s) indicated above, in my
name, to the area checked below. Enclosed is my remittance in the
amount of _____ for _____ packet(s) at $7.00 each.

_____ Africa   _____ Latin America

_____ Far East   _____ Near East

Name_____

Address_____

_____

NOTE: *This offer expires December 31, 1966.*